This Book Belongs to

Name ....

Address ....

....

Phone ....

Hospital name ....

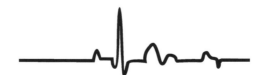

Summary

Patient name	Room n°	Page n°	Patient name	Room n°	Page n°
		1			56
		2			57
		3			58
		4			59
		5			60
		6			61
		7			62
		8			63
		9			64
		10			65
		11			66
		12			67
		13			68
		14			69
		15			70
		16			71
		17			72
		18			73
		19			74
		20			75
		21			76
		22			77
		23			78
		24			79
		25			80
		26			81
		27			82
		28			83
		29			84
		30			85
		31			86
		32			87
		33			88
		34			89
		35			90
		36			91
		37			92
		38			93
		39			94
		40			95
		41			96
		42			97
		43			98
		44			99
		45			100
		46			101
		47			102
		48			103
		49			104
		50			105
		51			106
		52			107
		53			108
		54			109
		55			110

Room	Admit Date	Situation	Attending Consult
Name	Allergies		
Age			
Sex	Code		

Hospital course	Present Illness	Precautions
	MD	

PMH : CA / CVA / DM / CHF / HTN / CKD / PVD / ESRD / Hypothyroid / Drug Abuse / PCI / Asthma / GERD / CAD / COPD / HLD / Psych / CKD / Smoker / Dementia / Other :

Tests/Procedures

Neuro	Neuro CIWA	Medical history					Lines
RASS		Meds/VF	Site	Size	Dose	Assessments	IV
NIH		1					CENTRAL
CAM		2					HD
A&O		3					Date
GCS		4					

Cardio/Tele	ACCU-CHECK			Medications
	Time	BS	Cover	
	Time	BS	Cover	
	Time	BS	Cover	

Respiratory	Vitals	GI:	LABS	
Loungs/02	P	Diet:	NA	WBC
	T O2	Last BM:	PH	PLT
	R BP	GU:	K	TROPONIN
			PT/INR	CR
Edema :	Skin :	Mobility :	BUN	CA
Musculoskeletal :			HGB	MG
			OTHER	

Pain Assess :	Pain Reassess :	Blood Sugar :	

Fluids:	Output:	Intake:	Notes :

DVT Pophylaxis:	

Plan of Care

Room	Admit Date	Situation	Attending Consult
Name	Allergies		
Age			
Sex	Code		

Hospital course	Present Illness	Precautions
	MD	

PMH : CA / CVA / DM / CHF / HTN / CKD / PVD / ESRD / Hypothyroid / Drug Abuse / PCI / Asthma / GERD / CAD / COPD / HLD / Psych / CKD / Smoker / Dementia / Other :

Tests/Procedures

Neuro	Neuro CIWA	Medical history					Lines
RASS		Meds/VF	Site	Size	Dose	Assessments	IV
NIH		1					CENTRAL
CAM		2					HD
A&O		3					Date
GCS		4					

Cardio/Tele	ACCU-CHECK			Medications
	Time	BS	Cover	
	Time	BS	Cover	
	Time	BS	Cover	

Respiratory		Vitals		GI:		LABS	
	Loungs/02	P	O2	Diet:		NA	WBC
		T		Last BM:		PH	PLT
			BP	GU:		K	TROPONIN
		R				PT/INR	CR
Edema :		Skin :		Mobility :		BUN	CA
Musculoskeletal :						HGB	MG
						OTHER	

Pain Assess :	Pain Reassess :	Blood Sugar :	

Fluids:	Output:	Intake:	Notes :
DVT Pophylaxis:			

Plan of Care

Room	Admit Date	Situation	Attending Consult
Name	Allergies		
Age			
Sex	Code		

Hospital course	Present Illness	Precautions
	MD	

PMH : CA / CVA / DM / CHF / HTN / CKD / PVD / ESRD / Hypothyroid / Drug Abuse / PCI / Asthma / GERD / CAD / COPD / HLD / Psych / CKD / Smoker / Dementia / Other :

Tests/Procedures

Neuro	Neuro CIWA	Medical history					Lines
RASS		Meds/VF	Site	Size	Dose	Assessments	IV
NIH		1					CENTRAL
CAM		2					HD
A&O		3					Date
GCS		4					

Cardio/Tele	ACCU-CHECK	Medications
	Time BS Cover	
	Time BS Cover	
	Time BS Cover	

Respiratory	Vitals	GI:	LABS	
Loungs/02	P O2	Diet:	NA	WBC
	T BP	Last BM:	PH	PLT
	R	GU:	K	TROPONIN
			PT/INR	CR
Edema :	Skin :	Mobility :	BUN	CA
Musculoskeletal :			HGB	MG
			OTHER	

Pain Assess :	Pain Reassess :	Blood Sugar :

Fluids:	Output:	Intake:	Notes :
DVT Pophylaxis:			

Plan of Care

Room	Admit Date	Situation	Attending Consult
Name	Allergies		
Age			
Sex	Code		

Hospital course	Present Illness	Precautions
	MD	

PMH : CA / CVA / DM / CHF / HTN / CKD / PVD / ESRD / Hypothyroid / Drug Abuse / PCI / Asthma / GERD / CAD / COPD / HLD / Psych / CKD / Smoker / Dementia / Other :

Tests/Procedures

Neuro	Neuro CIWA	Medical history					Lines
RASS		Meds/VF	Site	Size	Dose	Assessments	IV
NIH		1					CENTRAL
CAM		2					HD
A&O		3					Date
GCS		4					

Cardio/Tele	ACCU-CHECK			Medications
	Time	BS	Cover	
	Time	BS	Cover	
	Time	BS	Cover	

Respiratory		Vitals		GI:	LABS	
	Loungs/02	P		Diet:	NA	WBC
			O2	Last BM:	PH	PLT
		T		GU:	K	TROPONIN
			BP		PT/INR	CR
		R			BUN	CA

Edema :	Skin :	Mobility :	HGB	MG
Musculoskeletal :			OTHER	

Pain Assess :	Pain Reassess :	Blood Sugar :

Fluids:	Output:	Intake:	Notes :

DVT Pophylaxis:

Plan of Care

Room	Admit Date	Situation	Attending Consult
Name	Allergies		
Age			
Sex	Code		

Hospital course	Present Illness	Precautions
	MD	

PMH : CA / CVA / DM / CHF / HTN / CKD / PVD / ESRD / Hypothyroid / Drug Abuse / PCI / Asthma / GERD / CAD / COPD / HLD / Psych / CKD / Smoker / Dementia / Other :

Tests/Procedures

Neuro	Neuro CIWA	Medical history					Lines
RASS		Meds/VF	Site	Size	Dose	Assessments	IV
NIH		1					CENTRAL
CAM		2					HD
A&O		3					Date
GCS		4					

Cardio/Tele	ACCU-CHECK			Medications
	Time	BS	Cover	
	Time	BS	Cover	
	Time	BS	Cover	

Respiratory	Vitals	GI:	LABS	
Loungs/02	P O2	Diet:	NA	WBC
	T BP	Last BM:	PH	PLT
	R	GU:	K	TROPONIN
			PT/INR	CR
Edema :	Skin :	Mobility :	BUN	CA
Musculoskeletal :			HGB	MG
			OTHER	

Pain Assess :	Pain Reassess :	Blood Sugar :

Fluids:	Output:	Intake:	Notes :

DVT Pophylaxis:

Plan of Care

Room	Admit Date	Situation	Attending Consult
Name	**Allergies**		
Age			
Sex	**Code**		

Hospital course	**Present Illness**	**Precautions**
	MD	

PMH : CA / CVA / DM / CHF / HTN / CKD / PVD / ESRD / Hypothyroid / Drug Abuse / PCI / Asthma / GERD / CAD / COPD / HLD / Psych / CKD / Smoker / Dementia / Other :

Tests/Procedures

Neuro **Neuro CIWA**	**Medical history**					**Lines**
RASS	Meds/VF	Site	Size	Dose	Assessments	IV
NIH						CENTRAL
CAM	1					HD
A&O	2					Date
GCS	3					
	4					

Cardio/Tele	**ACCU-CHECK**			**Medications**
	Time	BS	Cover	
	Time	BS	Cover	
	Time	BS	Cover	

Respiratory	**Vitals**		**GI:**	**LABS**	
Loungs/02	P		Diet:	NA	WBC
		O2	Last BM:	PH	PLT
	T		**GU:**	K	TROPONIN
		BP		PT/INR	CR
	R			BUN	CA

Edema :	**Skin :**	**Mobility :**	HGB	MG

Musculoskeletal :		OTHER

Pain Assess :	**Pain Reassess :**	**Blood Sugar :**

Fluids:	**Output:**	**Intake:**	**Notes :**

DVT Pophylaxis:

Plan of Care

Room	Admit Date	Situation	Attending Consult
Name	Allergies		
Age			
Sex	Code		

Hospital course	Present Illness	Precautions
	MD	

PMH : CA / CVA / DM / CHF / HTN / CKD / PVD / ESRD / Hypothyroid / Drug Abuse / PCI / Asthma / GERD / CAD / COPD / HLD / Psych / CKD / Smoker / Dementia / Other :

Tests/Procedures

Neuro	Neuro CIWA	Medical history					Lines
RASS		Meds/VF	Site	Size	Dose	Assessments	IV
NIH		1					CENTRAL
CAM		2					HD
A&O		3					Date
GCS		4					

Cardio/Tele	ACCU-CHECK			Medications
	Time	BS	Cover	
	Time	BS	Cover	
	Time	BS	Cover	

Respiratory	Vitals	GI:	LABS	
Loungs/02	P O2	Diet:	NA	WBC
	T BP	Last BM:	PH	PLT
	R	GU:	K	TROPONIN
			PT/INR	CR
Edema :	Skin :	Mobility :	BUN	CA
Musculoskeletal :			HGB	MG
			OTHER	

Pain Assess :	Pain Reassess :	Blood Sugar :

Fluids:	Output:	Intake:	Notes :

DVT Pophylaxis:

Plan of Care

Room	Admit Date	Situation	Attending Consult
Name	Allergies		
Age			
Sex	Code		

Hospital course	Present Illness	Precautions
	MD	

PMH : CA / CVA / DM / CHF / HTN / CKD / PVD / ESRD / Hypothyroid / Drug Abuse / PCI / Asthma / GERD / CAD / COPD / HLD / Psych / CKD / Smoker / Dementia / Other :

Tests/Procedures

Neuro	Neuro CIWA	Medical history					Lines
RASS		Meds/VF	Site	Size	Dose	Assessments	IV
NIH		1					CENTRAL
CAM		2					HD
A&O		3					Date
GCS		4					

Cardio/Tele	ACCU-CHECK			Medications
	Time	BS	Cover	
	Time	BS	Cover	
	Time	BS	Cover	

Respiratory	Vitals	GI:	LABS	
Loungs/02	P	Diet:	NA	WBC
		O2	Last BM:	PH	PLT
	T	GU:	K	TROPONIN
	BP		PT/INR	CR
	R			

Edema :	Skin :	Mobility :	BUN	CA
Musculoskeletal :			HGB	MG
			OTHER	

Pain Assess :	Pain Reassess :	Blood Sugar :	

Fluids:	Output:	Intake:	Notes :
DVT Pophylaxis:			

Plan of Care

Room	Admit Date	Situation	Attending Consult
Name	Allergies		
Age			
Sex	Code		

Hospital course	Present Illness	Precautions
	MD	

PMH : CA / CVA / DM / CHF / HTN / CKD / PVD / ESRD / Hypothyroid / Drug Abuse / PCI / Asthma / GERD / CAD / COPD / HLD / Psych / CKD / Smoker / Dementia / Other :

Tests/Procedures

Neuro	Neuro CIWA	Medical history					Lines
RASS		Meds/VF	Site	Size	Dose	Assessments	IV
NIH		1					CENTRAL
CAM		2					HD
A&O		3					Date
GCS		4					

Cardio/Tele	ACCU-CHECK			Medications
	Time	BS	Cover	
	Time	BS	Cover	
	Time	BS	Cover	

Respiratory	Vitals	GI:	LABS	
Loungs/02	P	Diet:	NA	WBC
	O2	Last BM:	PH	PLT
	T	GU:	K	TROPONIN
	BP		PT/INR	CR
	R		BUN	CA

Edema :	Skin :	Mobility :	HGB	MG
Musculoskeletal :			OTHER	

Pain Assess :	Pain Reassess :	Blood Sugar :

Fluids:	Output:	Intake:	Notes :
DVT Pophylaxis:			

Plan of Care

Room	Admit Date	Situation	Attending Consult
Name	Allergies		
Age			
Sex	Code		

Hospital course	Present Illness	Precautions
	MD	

PMH : CA / CVA / DM / CHF / HTN / CKD / PVD / ESRD / Hypothyroid / Drug Abuse / PCI / Asthma / GERD / CAD / COPD / HLD / Psych / CKD / Smoker / Dementia / Other :

Tests/Procedures

Neuro	Neuro CIWA	Medical history					Lines
RASS		Meds/VF	Site	Size	Dose	Assessments	IV
NIH		1					CENTRAL
CAM		2					HD
A&O		3					Date
GCS		4					

Cardio/Tele	ACCU-CHECK			Medications
	Time	BS	Cover	
	Time	BS	Cover	
	Time	BS	Cover	

Respiratory		Vitals		GI:	LABS	
	Loungs/02	P		Diet:	NA	WBC
		T	O2	Last BM:	PH	PLT
			BP	GU:	K	TROPONIN
		R			PT/INR	CR
Edema :		Skin :		Mobility :	BUN	CA
Musculoskeletal :					HGB	MG
					OTHER	

Pain Assess :	Pain Reassess :	Blood Sugar :

Fluids:	Output:	Intake:	Notes :
DVT Pophylaxis:			

Plan of Care

10

Room	Admit Date	Situation	Attending Consult
Name	Allergies		
Age			
Sex	Code		

Hospital course	Present Illness	Precautions
	MD	

PMH : CA / CVA / DM / CHF / HTN / CKD / PVD / ESRD / Hypothyroid / Drug Abuse / PCI / Asthma / GERD / CAD / COPD / HLD / Psych / CKD / Smoker / Dementia / Other :

Tests/Procedures

Neuro	Neuro CIWA	Medical history					Lines
RASS		Meds/VF	Site	Size	Dose	Assessments	IV
NIH		1					CENTRAL
CAM		2					HD
A&O		3					Date
GCS		4					

Cardio/Tele	ACCU-CHECK			Medications
	Time	BS	Cover	
	Time	BS	Cover	
	Time	BS	Cover	

Respiratory	Vitals	GI:	LABS	
Loungs/02	P	Diet:	NA	WBC
	O2	Last BM:	PH	PLT
	T	GU:	K	TROPONIN
	BP		PT/INR	CR
	R		BUN	CA
Edema :	Skin :	Mobility :	HGB	MG
Musculoskeletal :			OTHER	

Pain Assess :	Pain Reassess :	Blood Sugar :

Fluids:	Output:	Intake:	Notes :
DVT Pophylaxis:			

Plan of Care

Room	Admit Date	Situation	Attending Consult
Name	Allergies		
Age			
Sex	Code		

Hospital course	Present Illness	Precautions
	MD	

PMH : CA / CVA / DM / CHF / HTN / CKD / PVD / ESRD / Hypothyroid / Drug Abuse / PCI / Asthma / GERD / CAD / COPD / HLD / Psych / CKD / Smoker / Dementia / Other :

Tests/Procedures

Neuro	Neuro CIWA	Medical history					Lines
RASS		Meds/VF	Site	Size	Dose	Assessments	IV
NIH		1					CENTRAL
CAM		2					HD
A&O		3					Date
GCS		4					

Cardio/Tele	ACCU-CHECK	Medications
	Time BS Cover	
	Time BS Cover	
	Time BS Cover	

Respiratory	Vitals	GI:	LABS	
Loungs/02	P O2	Diet:	NA	WBC
	T	Last BM:	PH	PLT
	BP	GU:	K	TROPONIN
	R		PT/INR	CR

Edema :	Skin :	Mobility :	BUN	CA
Musculoskeletal :			HGB	MG
			OTHER	

Pain Assess :	Pain Reassess :	Blood Sugar :

Fluids:	Output:	Intake:	Notes :
DVT Pophylaxis:			

Plan of Care

Room	Admit Date	Situation	Attending Consult
Name	Allergies		
Age			
Sex	Code		

Hospital course	Present Illness	Precautions
	MD	

PMH : CA / CVA / DM / CHF / HTN / CKD / PVD / ESRD / Hypothyroid / Drug Abuse / PCI / Asthma / GERD / CAD / COPD / HLD / Psych / CKD / Smoker / Dementia / Other :

Tests/Procedures

Neuro	Neuro CIWA	Medical history					Lines
RASS		Meds/VF	Site	Size	Dose	Assessments	IV
NIH		1					CENTRAL
CAM		2					HD
A&O		3					Date
GCS		4					

Cardio/Tele	ACCU-CHECK			Medications
	Time	BS	Cover	
	Time	BS	Cover	
	Time	BS	Cover	

Respiratory	Vitals	GI:	LABS	
Loungs/02	P	Diet:	NA	WBC
	O2	Last BM:	PH	PLT
	T	GU:	K	TROPONIN
	BP		PT/INR	CR
	R		BUN	CA

Edema :	Skin :	Mobility :	HGB	MG
Musculoskeletal :			OTHER	

Pain Assess :	Pain Reassess :	Blood Sugar :

Fluids:	Output:	Intake:	Notes :

DVT Pophylaxis:

Plan of Care

Room	Admit Date	Situation	Attending Consult
Name	Allergies		
Age			
Sex	Code		

Hospital course	Present Illness	Precautions
	MD	

PMH : CA / CVA / DM / CHF / HTN / CKD / PVD / ESRD / Hypothyroid / Drug Abuse / PCI / Asthma / GERD / CAD / COPD / HLD / Psych / CKD / Smoker / Dementia / Other :

Tests/Procedures

Neuro	Neuro CIWA	Medical history					Lines
RASS		Meds/VF	Site	Size	Dose	Assessments	IV
NIH		1					CENTRAL
CAM		2					HD
A&O		3					Date
GCS		4					

Cardio/Tele	ACCU-CHECK			Medications
	Time	BS	Cover	
	Time	BS	Cover	
	Time	BS	Cover	

Respiratory		Vitals		GI:		LABS	
	Loungs/02	P	O2	Diet:		NA	WBC
		T	BP	Last BM:		PH	PLT
		R		GU:		K	TROPONIN
						PT/INR	CR
Edema :	Skin :			Mobility :		BUN	CA
Musculoskeletal :						HGB	MG
						OTHER	

Pain Assess :	Pain Reassess :	Blood Sugar :

Fluids:	Output:	Intake:	Notes :
DVT Pophylaxis:			

Plan of Care

Room	Admit Date	Situation	Attending Consult
Name	Allergies		
Age			
Sex	Code		

Hospital course	Present Illness	Precautions
	MD	

PMH : CA / CVA / DM / CHF / HTN / CKD / PVD / ESRD / Hypothyroid / Drug Abuse / PCI / Asthma / GERD / CAD / COPD / HLD / Psych / CKD / Smoker / Dementia / Other :

Tests/Procedures

Neuro	Neuro CIWA	Medical history					Lines
RASS		Meds/VF	Site	Size	Dose	Assessments	IV
NIH		1					CENTRAL
CAM		2					HD
A&O		3					Date
GCS		4					

Cardio/Tele	ACCU-CHECK			Medications
	Time	BS	Cover	
	Time	BS	Cover	
	Time	BS	Cover	

Respiratory	Vitals	GI:	LABS	
Loungs/02	P	Diet:	NA	WBC
	O2		PH	PLT
	T	Last BM:	K	TROPONIN
	BP	GU:	PT/INR	CR
	R		BUN	CA
Edema : Skin :	Mobility :		HGB	MG
Musculoskeletal :			OTHER	

Pain Assess :	Pain Reassess :	Blood Sugar :

Fluids:	Output:	Intake:	Notes :
DVT Pophylaxis:			

Plan of Care

Room	Admit Date	Situation	Attending Consult
Name	Allergies		
Age			
Sex	Code		

Hospital course	Present Illness	Precautions
	MD	

PMH : CA / CVA / DM / CHF / HTN / CKD / PVD / ESRD / Hypothyroid / Drug Abuse / PCI / Asthma / GERD / CAD / COPD / HLD / Psych / CKD / Smoker / Dementia / Other :

Tests/Procedures

Neuro	Neuro CIWA	Medical history					Lines
RASS		Meds/VF	Site	Size	Dose	Assessments	IV
NIH		1					CENTRAL
CAM		2					HD
A&O		3					Date
GCS		4					

Cardio/Tele	ACCU-CHECK	Medications
	Time BS Cover	
	Time BS Cover	
	Time BS Cover	

Respiratory	Vitals	GI:	LABS	
Loungs/02	P O2	Diet:	NA	WBC
	T BP	Last BM:	PH	PLT
	R	GU:	K	TROPONIN
			PT/INR	CR
Edema :	Skin :	Mobility :	BUN	CA
Musculoskeletal :			HGB	MG
			OTHER	

Pain Assess :	Pain Reassess :	Blood Sugar :

Fluids:	Output:	Intake:	Notes :
DVT Pophylaxis:			

Plan of Care

Room	Admit Date	Situation	Attending Consult
Name	Allergies		
Age			
Sex	Code		

Hospital course	Present Illness	Precautions
	MD	

PMH : CA / CVA / DM / CHF / HTN / CKD / PVD / ESRD / Hypothyroid / Drug Abuse / PCI / Asthma / GERD / CAD / COPD / HLD / Psych / CKD / Smoker / Dementia / Other :

Tests/Procedures

Neuro	Neuro CIWA	Medical history					Lines
RASS		Meds/VF	Site	Size	Dose	Assessments	IV
NIH		1					CENTRAL
CAM		2					HD
A&O		3					Date
GCS		4					

Cardio/Tele	ACCU-CHECK			Medications
	Time	BS	Cover	
	Time	BS	Cover	
	Time	BS	Cover	

Respiratory	Vitals	GI:	LABS	
Loungs/02	P	Diet:	NA	WBC
	O2	Last BM:	PH	PLT
	T	GU:	K	TROPONIN
	BP		PT/INR	CR
	R		BUN	CA
Edema :	Skin :	Mobility :	HGB	MG
Musculoskeletal :			OTHER	

Pain Assess :	Pain Reassess :	Blood Sugar :

Fluids:	Output:	Intake:	Notes :
DVT Pophylaxis:			

Plan of Care

Room	Admit Date	Situation	Attending Consult
Name	Allergies		
Age			
Sex	Code		

Hospital course	Present Illness	Precautions
	MD	

PMH : CA / CVA / DM / CHF / HTN / CKD / PVD / ESRD / Hypothyroid / Drug Abuse / PCI / Asthma / GERD / CAD / COPD / HLD / Psych / CKD / Smoker / Dementia / Other :

Tests/Procedures

Neuro	Neuro CIWA	Medical history					Lines
RASS		Meds/VF	Site	Size	Dose	Assessments	IV
NIH		1					CENTRAL
CAM		2					HD
A&O		3					Date
GCS		4					

Cardio/Tele	ACCU-CHECK			Medications
	Time	BS	Cover	
	Time	BS	Cover	
	Time	BS	Cover	

Respiratory		Vitals		GI:		LABS	
Loungs/02		P	O2	Diet:		NA	WBC
		T	BP	Last BM:		PH	PLT
		R		GU:		K	TROPONIN
						PT/INR	CR
Edema :	Skin :			Mobility :		BUN	CA
Musculoskeletal :						HGB	MG
						OTHER	

Pain Assess :	Pain Reassess :	Blood Sugar :

Fluids:	Output:	Intake:	Notes :
DVT Pophylaxis:			

Plan of Care

Room	Admit Date	Situation	Attending Consult
Name	Allergies		
Age			
Sex	Code		

Hospital course	Present Illness	Precautions
	MD	

PMH : CA / CVA / DM / CHF / HTN / CKD / PVD / ESRD / Hypothyroid / Drug Abuse / PCI / Asthma / GERD / CAD / COPD / HLD / Psych / CKD / Smoker / Dementia / Other :

Tests/Procedures

Neuro	Neuro CIWA	Medical history					Lines
RASS		Meds/VF	Site	Size	Dose	Assessments	IV
NIH		1					CENTRAL
CAM		2					HD
A&O		3					Date
GCS		4					

Cardio/Tele	ACCU-CHECK	Medications
	Time BS Cover	
	Time BS Cover	
	Time BS Cover	

Respiratory	Vitals	GI:	LABS	
Loungs/02	P	Diet:	NA	WBC
	O2	Last BM:	PH	PLT
	T	GU:	K	TROPONIN
	BP		PT/INR	CR
	R			
Edema :	Skin :	Mobility :	BUN	CA
Musculoskeletal :			HGB	MG
			OTHER	

Pain Assess :	Pain Reassess :	Blood Sugar :

Fluids:	Output:	Intake:	Notes :

DVT Pophylaxis:

Plan of Care

Room	Admit Date	Situation	Attending Consult
Name	**Allergies**		
Age			
Sex	**Code**		

Hospital course	Present Illness	Precautions
	MD	

PMH : CA / CVA / DM / CHF / HTN / CKD / PVD / ESRD / Hypothyroid / Drug Abuse / PCI / Asthma / GERD / CAD / COPD / HLD / Psych / CKD / Smoker / Dementia / Other :

Tests/Procedures

Neuro	Neuro CIWA	Medical history					Lines
RASS		Meds/VF	Site	Size	Dose	Assessments	IV
NIH		1					CENTRAL
CAM		2					HD
A&O		3					Date
GCS		4					

Cardio/Tele	ACCU-CHECK			Medications
	Time	BS	Cover	
	Time	BS	Cover	
	Time	BS	Cover	

Respiratory	Vitals	GI:	LABS	
Loungs/02	P O2	Diet:	NA	WBC
	T BP	Last BM:	PH	PLT
	R	GU:	K	TROPONIN
			PT/INR	CR
Edema : **Skin :** **Mobility :**			BUN	CA
Musculoskeletal :			HGB	MG
			OTHER	

Pain Assess :	Pain Reassess :	Blood Sugar :

Fluids:	Output:	Intake:	Notes :
DVT Pophylaxis:			

Plan of Care

Room	Admit Date	Situation	Attending Consult
Name	Allergies		
Age			
Sex	Code		

Hospital course	Present Illness	Precautions
	MD	

PMH : CA / CVA / DM / CHF / HTN / CKD / PVD / ESRD / Hypothyroid / Drug Abuse / PCI / Asthma / GERD / CAD / COPD / HLD / Psych / CKD / Smoker / Dementia / Other :

Tests/Procedures

Neuro	Neuro CIWA	Medical history					Lines
RASS		Meds/VF	Site	Size	Dose	Assessments	IV
NIH		1					CENTRAL
CAM		2					HD
A&O		3					Date
GCS		4					

Cardio/Tele	ACCU–CHECK			Medications
	Time	BS	Cover	
	Time	BS	Cover	
	Time	BS	Cover	

Respiratory	Vitals	GI:	LABS	
Loungs/02	P	Diet:	NA	WBC
	O2	Last BM:	PH	PLT
	T	GU:	K	TROPONIN
	BP		PT/INR	CR
	R		BUN	CA
Edema :	Skin :	Mobility :	HGB	MG
Musculoskeletal :			OTHER	

Pain Assess :	Pain Reassess :	Blood Sugar :	

Fluids:	Output:	Intake:	Notes :
DVT Pophylaxis:			

Plan of Care

Room	Admit Date	Situation	Attending Consult
Name	Allergies		
Age			
Sex	Code		

Hospital course	Present Illness	Precautions
	MD	

PMH : CA / CVA / DM / CHF / HTN / CKD / PVD / ESRD / Hypothyroid / Drug Abuse / PCI / Asthma / GERD / CAD / COPD / HLD / Psych / CKD / Smoker / Dementia / Other :

Tests/Procedures

Neuro	Neuro CIWA	Medical history					Lines
RASS		Meds/VF	Site	Size	Dose	Assessments	IV
NIH		1					CENTRAL
CAM		2					HD
A&O		3					Date
GCS		4					

Cardio/Tele	ACCU-CHECK			Medications
	Time	BS	Cover	
	Time	BS	Cover	
	Time	BS	Cover	

Respiratory	Vitals	GI:	LABS	
Loungs/02	P O2	Diet:	NA	WBC
	T	Last BM:	PH	PLT
	R BP	GU:	K	TROPONIN
			PT/INR	CR

Edema :	Skin :	Mobility :	BUN	CA
Musculoskeletal :			HGB	MG
			OTHER	

Pain Assess :	Pain Reassess :	Blood Sugar :

Fluids:	Output:	Intake:	Notes :
DVT Pophylaxis:			

Plan of Care

Room	Admit Date	Situation	Attending Consult
Name	Allergies		
Age			
Sex	Code		

Hospital course	Present Illness	Precautions
	MD	

PMH : CA / CVA / DM / CHF / HTN / CKD / PVD / ESRD / Hypothyroid / Drug Abuse / PCI / Asthma / GERD / CAD / COPD / HLD / Psych / CKD / Smoker / Dementia / Other :

Tests/Procedures

Neuro	Neuro CIWA	Medical history					Lines
RASS		Meds/VF	Site	Size	Dose	Assessments	IV
NIH		1					CENTRAL
CAM		2					HD
A&O		3					Date
GCS		4					

Cardio/Tele	ACCU-CHECK			Medications
	Time	BS	Cover	
	Time	BS	Cover	
	Time	BS	Cover	

Respiratory	Vitals	GI:	LABS	
Loungs/02	P O2	Diet:	NA	WBC
	T BP	Last BM:	PH	PLT
	R	GU:	K	TROPONIN
			PT/INR	CR
Edema :	Skin :	Mobility :	BUN	CA
			HGB	MG
Musculoskeletal :			OTHER	

Pain Assess :	Pain Reassess :	Blood Sugar :

Fluids:	Output:	Intake:	Notes :
DVT Pophylaxis:			

Plan of Care

Room	Admit Date	Situation	Attending Consult
Name	Allergies		
Age			
Sex	Code		

Hospital course	Present Illness	Precautions
	MD	

PMH : CA / CVA / DM / CHF / HTN / CKD / PVD / ESRD / Hypothyroid / Drug Abuse / PCI / Asthma / GERD / CAD / COPD / HLD / Psych / CKD / Smoker / Dementia / Other :

Tests/Procedures

Neuro	Neuro CIWA	Medical history					Lines
RASS		Meds/VF	Site	Size	Dose	Assessments	IV
NIH		1					CENTRAL
CAM		2					HD
A&O		3					Date
GCS		4					

Cardio/Tele	ACCU-CHECK			Medications
	Time	BS	Cover	
	Time	BS	Cover	
	Time	BS	Cover	

Respiratory	Vitals	GI:	LABS	
Loungs/02	P O2	Diet:	NA	WBC
	T	Last BM:	PH	PLT
	BP	GU:	K	TROPONIN
	R		PT/INR	CR

Edema :	Skin :	Mobility :	BUN	CA

Musculoskeletal :

HGB	MG
OTHER	

Pain Assess :	Pain Reassess :	Blood Sugar :	

Fluids:	Output:	Intake:	Notes :

DVT Pophylaxis:

Plan of Care

Room	Admit Date	Situation	Attending Consult
Name	Allergies		
Age			
Sex	Code		

Hospital course	Present Illness	Precautions
	MD	

PMH : CA / CVA / DM / CHF / HTN / CKD / PVD / ESRD / Hypothyroid / Drug Abuse / PCI / Asthma / GERD / CAD / COPD / HLD / Psych / CKD / Smoker / Dementia / Other :

Tests/Procedures

Neuro	Neuro CIWA	Medical history					Lines
RASS		Meds/VF	Site	Size	Dose	Assessments	IV
NIH		1					CENTRAL
CAM		2					HD
A&O		3					Date
GCS		4					

Cardio/Tele	ACCU-CHECK			Medications
	Time	BS	Cover	
	Time	BS	Cover	
	Time	BS	Cover	

Respiratory	Vitals	GI:	LABS	
Loungs/02	P O2	Diet:	NA	WBC
	T BP	Last BM:	PH	PLT
	R	GU:	K	TROPONIN
			PT/INR	CR
Edema :	Skin :	Mobility :	BUN	CA
Musculoskeletal :			HGB	MG
			OTHER	

Pain Assess :	Pain Reassess :	Blood Sugar :

Fluids:	Output:	Intake:	Notes :

DVT Pophylaxis:

Plan of Care

Room	Admit Date	Situation	Attending Consult
Name	**Allergies**		
Age			
Sex	**Code**		

Hospital course	Present Illness	Precautions
	MD	

PMH : CA / CVA / DM / CHF / HTN / CKD / PVD / ESRD / Hypothyroid / Drug Abuse / PCI / Asthma / GERD / CAD / COPD / HLD / Psych / CKD / Smoker / Dementia / Other :

Tests/Procedures

Neuro	Neuro CIWA	Medical history					Lines
RASS		Meds/VF	Site	Size	Dose	Assessments	IV
NIH		1					CENTRAL
CAM		2					HD
A&O		3					Date
GCS		4					

Cardio/Tele	ACCU-CHECK			Medications
	Time	BS	Cover	
	Time	BS	Cover	
	Time	BS	Cover	

Respiratory	Vitals	GI:	LABS	
Loungs/02	P	Diet:	NA	WBC
	T O2	Last BM:	PH	PLT
	BP	GU:	K	TROPONIN
	R		PT/INR	CR

Edema :   **Skin :**   **Mobility :**

BUN	CA
HGB	MG
OTHER	

Musculoskeletal :

Pain Assess :	Pain Reassess :	Blood Sugar :

Fluids:	Output:	Intake:	Notes :

DVT Pophylaxis:

Plan of Care

Room	Admit Date	Situation	Attending Consult
Name	Allergies		
Age			
Sex	Code		

Hospital course	Present Illness	Precautions
	MD	

PMH : CA / CVA / DM / CHF / HTN / CKD / PVD / ESRD / Hypothyroid / Drug Abuse / PCI / Asthma / GERD / CAD / COPD / HLD / Psych / CKD / Smoker / Dementia / Other :

Tests/Procedures

Neuro	Neuro CIWA	Medical history					Lines
RASS		Meds/VF	Site	Size	Dose	Assessments	IV
NIH		1					CENTRAL
CAM		2					HD
A&O		3					Date
GCS		4					

Cardio/Tele	ACCU-CHECK			Medications
	Time	BS	Cover	
	Time	BS	Cover	
	Time	BS	Cover	

Respiratory	Vitals	GI:	LABS	
Loungs/02	P O2	Diet:	NA	WBC
	T BP	Last BM:	PH	PLT
	R	GU:	K	TROPONIN
			PT/INR	CR
Edema :	Skin :	Mobility :	BUN	CA
Musculoskeletal :			HGB	MG
			OTHER	

Pain Assess :	Pain Reassess :	Blood Sugar :

Fluids:	Output:	Intake:	Notes :

DVT Pophylaxis:

Plan of Care

Room	Admit Date	Situation	Attending Consult
Name	Allergies		
Age			
Sex	Code		

Hospital course	Present Illness	Precautions
	MD	

PMH : CA / CVA / DM / CHF / HTN / CKD / PVD / ESRD / Hypothyroid / Drug Abuse / PCI / Asthma / GERD / CAD / COPD / HLD / Psych / CKD / Smoker / Dementia / Other :

Tests/Procedures

Neuro	Neuro CIWA	Medical history					Lines
RASS		Meds/VF	Site	Size	Dose	Assessments	IV
NIH		1					CENTRAL
CAM		2					HD
A&O		3					Date
GCS		4					

Cardio/Tele	ACCU-CHECK			Medications
	Time	BS	Cover	
	Time	BS	Cover	
	Time	BS	Cover	

Respiratory	Vitals	GI:	LABS	
Loungs/02	P	Diet:	NA	WBC
		O2		PH	PLT
	T	Last BM:	K	TROPONIN
	BP	GU:	PT/INR	CR
	R		BUN	CA

Edema :	Skin :	Mobility :	HGB	MG
			OTHER	

Musculoskeletal :

Pain Assess :	Pain Reassess :	Blood Sugar :

Fluids:	Output:	Intake:	Notes :

DVT Pophylaxis:

Plan of Care

Room	Admit Date	Situation	Attending Consult
Name	Allergies		
Age			
Sex	Code		

Hospital course	Present Illness	Precautions
	MD	

PMH : CA / CVA / DM / CHF / HTN / CKD / PVD / ESRD / Hypothyroid / Drug Abuse / PCI / Asthma / GERD / CAD / COPD / HLD / Psych / CKD / Smoker / Dementia / Other :

Tests/Procedures

Neuro	Neuro CIWA	Medical history					Lines
RASS		Meds/VF	Site	Size	Dose	Assessments	IV
NIH		1					CENTRAL
CAM		2					HD
A&O		3					Date
GCS		4					

Cardio/Tele	ACCU-CHECK			Medications
	Time	BS	Cover	
	Time	BS	Cover	
	Time	BS	Cover	

Respiratory	Vitals	GI:	LABS	
Loungs/02	P O2	Diet:	NA	WBC
	T BP	Last BM:	PH	PLT
	R	GU:	K	TROPONIN
			PT/INR	CR
Edema :	Skin :	Mobility :	BUN	CA
Musculoskeletal :			HGB	MG
			OTHER	

Pain Assess :	Pain Reassess :	Blood Sugar :

Fluids:	Output:	Intake:	Notes :

DVT Pophylaxis:

Plan of Care

Room	Admit Date	Situation	Attending Consult
Name	**Allergies**		
Age			
Sex	**Code**		

Hospital course	**Present Illness**	**Precautions**
	MD	

PMH : CA / CVA / DM / CHF / HTN / CKD / PVD / ESRD / Hypothyroid / Drug Abuse / PCI / Asthma / GERD / CAD / COPD / HLD / Psych / CKD / Smoker / Dementia / Other :

Tests/Procedures

Neuro	Neuro CIWA	Medical history					Lines
RASS		Meds/VF	Site	Size	Dose	Assessments	IV
NIH		1					CENTRAL
CAM		2					HD
A&O		3					Date
GCS		4					

Cardio/Tele	ACCU-CHECK	Medications
	Time BS Cover	
	Time BS Cover	
	Time BS Cover	

Respiratory	Vitals	GI:	LABS	
Loungs/02	P O2	Diet:	NA	WBC
		Last BM:	PH	PLT
	T BP	GU:	K	TROPONIN
	R		PT/INR	CR
Edema :	**Skin :**	**Mobility :**	BUN	CA
Musculoskeletal :			HGB	MG
			OTHER	

Pain Assess :	Pain Reassess :	Blood Sugar :

Fluids:	Output:	Intake:	Notes :
DVT Pophylaxis:			

Plan of Care

Room	Admit Date	Situation	Attending Consult
Name	Allergies		
Age			
Sex	Code		

Hospital course	Present Illness	Precautions
	MD	

PMH : CA / CVA / DM / CHF / HTN / CKD / PVD / ESRD / Hypothyroid / Drug Abuse / PCI / Asthma / GERD / CAD / COPD / HLD / Psych / CKD / Smoker / Dementia / Other :

Tests/Procedures

Neuro	Neuro CIWA	Medical history					Lines
RASS		Meds/VF	Site	Size	Dose	Assessments	IV
NIH		1					CENTRAL
CAM		2					HD
A&O		3					Date
GCS		4					

Cardio/Tele	ACCU-CHECK	Medications
	Time BS Cover	
	Time BS Cover	
	Time BS Cover	

Respiratory	Vitals	GI:	LABS	
Loungs/02	P O2 T BP R	Diet: Last BM: GU:	NA	WBC
			PH	PLT
			K	TROPONIN
			PT/INR	CR

Edema :	Skin :	Mobility :	BUN	CA
Musculoskeletal :			HGB	MG
			OTHER	

Pain Assess :	Pain Reassess :	Blood Sugar :	

Fluids:	Output:	Intake:	Notes :
DVT Pophylaxis:			

Plan of Care

Room	Admit Date	Situation	Attending Consult
Name	Allergies		
Age			
Sex	Code		

Hospital course	Present Illness	Precautions
	MD	

PMH : CA / CVA / DM / CHF / HTN / CKD / PVD / ESRD / Hypothyroid / Drug Abuse / PCI / Asthma / GERD / CAD / COPD / HLD / Psych / CKD / Smoker / Dementia / Other :

Tests/Procedures

Neuro	Neuro CIWA	Medical history					Lines
RASS		Meds/VF	Site	Size	Dose	Assessments	IV
NIH		1					CENTRAL
CAM		2					HD
A&O		3					Date
GCS		4					

Cardio/Tele	ACCU-CHECK	Medications
	Time BS Cover	
	Time BS Cover	
	Time BS Cover	

Respiratory	Vitals	GI:	LABS	
Loungs/02	P O2 T BP R	Diet: Last BM: GU:	NA	WBC
			PH	PLT
			K	TROPONIN
Edema : Skin : Mobility :			PT/INR	CR
			BUN	CA
Musculoskeletal :			HGB	MG
			OTHER	

Pain Assess :	Pain Reassess :	Blood Sugar :

Fluids:	Output:	Intake:	Notes :
DVT Pophylaxis:			

Plan of Care

Room	Admit Date	Situation	Attending Consult
Name	Allergies		
Age			
Sex	Code		

Hospital course	Present Illness	Precautions
	MD	

PMH : CA / CVA / DM / CHF / HTN / CKD / PVD / ESRD / Hypothyroid / Drug Abuse / PCI / Asthma / GERD / CAD / COPD / HLD / Psych / CKD / Smoker / Dementia / Other :

Tests/Procedures

Neuro	Neuro CIWA	Medical history					Lines
RASS		Meds/VF	Site	Size	Dose	Assessments	IV
NIH		1					CENTRAL
CAM		2					HD
A&O		3					Date
GCS		4					

Cardio/Tele	ACCU-CHECK			Medications
	Time	BS	Cover	
	Time	BS	Cover	
	Time	BS	Cover	

Respiratory	Vitals	GI:	LABS	
Loungs/02	P		Diet:	NA	WBC

Respiratory						
Loungs/02	P	O2	Diet:	NA		WBC
	T	BP	Last BM:	PH		PLT
	R		GU:	K		TROPONIN
				PT/INR		CR
Edema :	Skin :		Mobility :	BUN		CA
Musculoskeletal :				HGB		MG
				OTHER		

Pain Assess :	Pain Reassess :	Blood Sugar :

Fluids:	Output:	Intake:	Notes :

DVT Pophylaxis:

Plan of Care

Room		Admit Date		Situation		Attending Consult	
Name		**Allergies**					
Age							
Sex		**Code**					

Hospital course	**Present Illness**	**Precautions**
	MD	

PMH : CA / CVA / DM / CHF / HTN / CKD / PVD / ESRD / Hypothyroid / Drug Abuse / PCI / Asthma / GERD / CAD / COPD / HLD / Psych / CKD / Smoker / Dementia / Other :

Tests/Procedures

Neuro	Neuro CIWA	Medical history					Lines
RASS		Meds/VF	Site	Size	Dose	Assessments	IV
NIH		1					CENTRAL
CAM		2					HD
A&O		3					Date
GCS		4					

Cardio/Tele	ACCU-CHECK			Medications
	Time	BS	Cover	
	Time	BS	Cover	
	Time	BS	Cover	

Respiratory		Vitals		GI:	LABS	
	Loungs/02	P	O2	Diet:	NA	WBC
		T	BP	Last BM:	PH	PLT
		R		GU:	K	TROPONIN
					PT/INR	CR
Edema :	**Skin :**			**Mobility :**	BUN	CA
					HGB	MG
Musculoskeletal :					OTHER	

Pain Assess :	**Pain Reassess :**	**Blood Sugar :**

Fluids:	**Output:**	**Intake:**	**Notes :**

DVT Pophylaxis:

Plan of Care

Room	Admit Date	Situation	Attending Consult
Name	Allergies		
Age			
Sex	Code		

Hospital course	Present Illness	Precautions
	MD	

PMH : CA / CVA / DM / CHF / HTN / CKD / PVD / ESRD / Hypothyroid / Drug Abuse / PCI / Asthma / GERD / CAD / COPD / HLD / Psych / CKD / Smoker / Dementia / Other :

Tests/Procedures

Neuro	Neuro CIWA	Medical history					Lines
RASS		Meds/VF	Site	Size	Dose	Assessments	IV
NIH		1					CENTRAL
CAM		2					HD
A&O		3					Date
GCS		4					

Cardio/Tele	ACCU-CHECK			Medications
	Time	BS	Cover	
	Time	BS	Cover	
	Time	BS	Cover	

Respiratory	Vitals	GI:	LABS	
Loungs/02	P	Diet:	NA	WBC
	O2	Last BM:	PH	PLT
	T	GU:	K	TROPONIN
	BP		PT/INR	CR
	R		BUN	CA
Edema :	Skin :	Mobility :	HGB	MG
Musculoskeletal :			OTHER	

Pain Assess :	Pain Reassess :	Blood Sugar :

Fluids:	Output:	Intake:	Notes :
DVT Pophylaxis:			

Plan of Care

Room	Admit Date	Situation	Attending Consult
Name	Allergies		
Age			
Sex	Code		

Hospital course	Present Illness	Precautions
	MD	

PMH : CA / CVA / DM / CHF / HTN / CKD / PVD / ESRD / Hypothyroid / Drug Abuse / PCI / Asthma / GERD / CAD / COPD / HLD / Psych / CKD / Smoker / Dementia / Other :

Tests/Procedures

Neuro	Neuro CIWA	Medical history					Lines
RASS		Meds/VF	Site	Size	Dose	Assessments	IV
NIH		1					CENTRAL
CAM		2					HD
A&O		3					Date
GCS		4					

Cardio/Tele	ACCU-CHECK			Medications
	Time	BS	Cover	
	Time	BS	Cover	
	Time	BS	Cover	

Respiratory	Vitals	GI:	LABS	
Loungs/02	P	Diet:	NA	WBC
		O2	Last BM:	PH	PLT
	T	GU:	K	TROPONIN
		BP		PT/INR	CR
	R		BUN	CA

Edema :	Skin :	Mobility :	HGB	MG
Musculoskeletal :			OTHER	

Pain Assess :	Pain Reassess :	Blood Sugar :

Fluids:	Output:	Intake:	Notes :

DVT Pophylaxis:

Plan of Care

Room	Admit Date	Situation	Attending Consult
Name	Allergies		
Age			
Sex	Code		

Hospital course	Present Illness	Precautions
	MD	

PMH : CA / CVA / DM / CHF / HTN / CKD / PVD / ESRD / Hypothyroid / Drug Abuse / PCI / Asthma / GERD / CAD / COPD / HLD / Psych / CKD / Smoker / Dementia / Other :

Tests/Procedures

Neuro	Neuro CIWA	Medical history					Lines
RASS		Meds/VF	Site	Size	Dose	Assessments	IV
NIH		1					CENTRAL
CAM		2					HD
A&O		3					Date
GCS		4					

Cardio/Tele	ACCU-CHECK			Medications
	Time	BS	Cover	
	Time	BS	Cover	
	Time	BS	Cover	

Respiratory	Vitals	GI:	LABS	
Loungs/02	P O2	Diet:	NA	WBC
	T BP	Last BM:	PH	PLT
	R	GU:	K	TROPONIN
			PT/INR	CR
Edema :	Skin :	Mobility :	BUN	CA
Musculoskeletal :			HGB	MG
			OTHER	

Pain Assess :	Pain Reassess :	Blood Sugar :

Fluids:	Output:	Intake:	Notes :

DVT Pophylaxis:

Plan of Care

Room	Admit Date	Situation	Attending Consult
Name	Allergies		
Age			
Sex	Code		

Hospital course	Present Illness	Precautions
	MD	

PMH : CA / CVA / DM / CHF / HTN / CKD / PVD / ESRD / Hypothyroid / Drug Abuse / PCI / Asthma / GERD / CAD / COPD / HLD / Psych / CKD / Smoker / Dementia / Other :

Tests/Procedures

Neuro	Neuro CIWA	Medical history					Lines
RASS		Meds/VF	Site	Size	Dose	Assessments	IV
NIH		1					CENTRAL
CAM		2					HD
A&O		3					Date
GCS		4					

Cardio/Tele	ACCU-CHECK			Medications
	Time	BS	Cover	
	Time	BS	Cover	
	Time	BS	Cover	

Respiratory	Vitals	GI:	LABS	
Loungs/02	P	Diet:	NA	WBC
	O2	Last BM:	PH	PLT
	T	GU:	K	TROPONIN
	BP		PT/INR	CR
	R		BUN	CA
Edema :	Skin :	Mobility :	HGB	MG
			OTHER	

Musculoskeletal :

Pain Assess :	Pain Reassess :	Blood Sugar :

Fluids:	Output:	Intake:	Notes :

DVT Pophylaxis:

Plan of Care

Room	Admit Date	Situation	Attending Consult
Name	Allergies		
Age			
Sex	Code		

Hospital course	Present Illness	Precautions
	MD	

PMH : CA / CVA / DM / CHF / HTN / CKD / PVD / ESRD / Hypothyroid / Drug Abuse / PCI / Asthma / GERD / CAD / COPD / HLD / Psych / CKD / Smoker / Dementia / Other :

Tests/Procedures

Neuro	Neuro CIWA	Medical history					Lines
RASS		Meds/VF	Site	Size	Dose	Assessments	IV
NIH		1					CENTRAL
CAM		2					HD
A&O		3					Date
GCS		4					

Cardio/Tele	ACCU-CHECK			Medications
	Time	BS	Cover	
	Time	BS	Cover	
	Time	BS	Cover	

Respiratory	Vitals	GI:	LABS	
Lounges/02	P	Diet:	NA	WBC
	O2	Last BM:	PH	PLT
	T	GU:	K	TROPONIN
	BP		PT/INR	CR
	R		BUN	CA

Edema :	Skin :	Mobility :	HGB	MG
Musculoskeletal :			OTHER	

Pain Assess :	Pain Reassess :	Blood Sugar :

Fluids:	Output:	Intake:	Notes :
DVT Pophylaxis:			

Plan of Care

Room	Admit Date	Situation	Attending Consult
Name	**Allergies**		
Age			
Sex	**Code**		

Hospital course	Present Illness	Precautions
	MD	

PMH : CA / CVA / DM / CHF / HTN / CKD / PVD / ESRD / Hypothyroid / Drug Abuse / PCI / Asthma / GERD / CAD / COPD / HLD / Psych / CKD / Smoker / Dementia / Other :

Tests/Procedures

Neuro	Neuro CIWA	Medical history					Lines
RASS		Meds/VF	Site	Size	Dose	Assessments	IV
NIH		1					CENTRAL
CAM		2					HD
A&O		3					Date
GCS		4					

Cardio/Tele	ACCU-CHECK	Medications
	Time BS Cover	
	Time BS Cover	
	Time BS Cover	

Respiratory	Vitals	GI:	LABS	
Loungs/02	P O2	Diet:	NA	WBC
	T BP	Last BM:	PH	PLT
	R	GU:	K	TROPONIN
			PT/INR	CR

Edema :	Skin :	Mobility :	BUN	CA
			HGB	MG

Musculoskeletal :

OTHER

Pain Assess :	Pain Reassess :	Blood Sugar :

Fluids:	Output:	Intake:	Notes :

DVT Pophylaxis:

Plan of Care

Room	Admit Date	Situation	Attending Consult
Name	Allergies		
Age			
Sex	Code		

Hospital course	Present Illness	Precautions
	MD	

PMH : CA / CVA / DM / CHF / HTN / CKD / PVD / ESRD / Hypothyroid / Drug Abuse / PCI / Asthma / GERD / CAD / COPD / HLD / Psych / CKD / Smoker / Dementia / Other :

Tests/Procedures

Neuro	Neuro CIWA	Medical history					Lines
RASS		Meds/VF	Site	Size	Dose	Assessments	IV
NIH		1					CENTRAL
CAM		2					HD
A&O		3					Date
GCS		4					

Cardio/Tele	ACCU-CHECK			Medications
	Time	BS	Cover	
	Time	BS	Cover	
	Time	BS	Cover	

Respiratory	Vitals	GI:	LABS	
Loungs/02	P	Diet:	NA	WBC
	O2	Last BM:	PH	PLT
	T	GU:	K	TROPONIN
	BP		PT/INR	CR
	R		BUN	CA

Edema :	Skin :	Mobility :	HGB	MG
Musculoskeletal :			OTHER	

Pain Assess :	Pain Reassess :	Blood Sugar :	

Fluids:	Output:	Intake:	Notes :

DVT Pophylaxis:

Plan of Care

Room	Admit Date	Situation	Attending Consult
Name	Allergies		
Age			
Sex	Code		

Hospital course	Present Illness	Precautions
	MD	

PMH : CA / CVA / DM / CHF / HTN / CKD / PVD / ESRD / Hypothyroid / Drug Abuse / PCI / Asthma / GERD / CAD / COPD / HLD / Psych / CKD / Smoker / Dementia / Other :

Tests/Procedures

Neuro	Neuro CIWA	Medical history					Lines
RASS		Meds/VF	Site	Size	Dose	Assessments	IV
NIH		1					CENTRAL
CAM		2					HD
A&O		3					Date
GCS		4					

Cardio/Tele	ACCU-CHECK			Medications
	Time	BS	Cover	
	Time	BS	Cover	
	Time	BS	Cover	

Respiratory	Vitals	GI:	LABS	
Loungs/02	P O2	Diet:	NA	WBC
	T BP	Last BM:	PH	PLT
	R	GU:	K	TROPONIN
			PT/INR	CR

Edema :	Skin :	Mobility :	BUN	CA
Musculoskeletal :			HGB	MG
			OTHER	

Pain Assess :	Pain Reassess :	Blood Sugar :

Fluids:	Output:	Intake:	Notes :
DVT Pophylaxis:			

Plan of Care

Room	Admit Date	Situation	Attending Consult
Name	Allergies		
Age			
Sex	Code		

Hospital course	Present Illness	Precautions
	MD	

PMH : CA / CVA / DM / CHF / HTN / CKD / PVD / ESRD / Hypothyroid / Drug Abuse / PCI / Asthma / GERD / CAD / COPD / HLD / Psych / CKD / Smoker / Dementia / Other :

Tests/Procedures

Neuro	Neuro CIWA	Medical history					Lines
RASS		Meds/VF	Site	Size	Dose	Assessments	IV
NIH		1					CENTRAL
CAM		2					HD
A&O		3					Date
GCS		4					

Cardio/Tele	ACCU-CHECK			Medications
	Time	BS	Cover	
	Time	BS	Cover	
	Time	BS	Cover	

Respiratory	Vitals	GI:	LABS	
Loungs/02	P O2 T BP R	Diet: Last BM: GU:	NA	WBC
			PH	PLT
			K	TROPONIN
			PT/INR	CR

Edema :	Skin :	Mobility :	BUN	CA
			HGB	MG

Musculoskeletal :		OTHER

Pain Assess :	Pain Reassess :	Blood Sugar :

Fluids:	Output:	Intake:	Notes :

DVT Pophylaxis:	

Plan of Care

Room	Admit Date	Situation	Attending Consult
Name	Allergies		
Age			
Sex	Code		

Hospital course	Present Illness	Precautions
	MD	

PMH : CA / CVA / DM / CHF / HTN / CKD / PVD / ESRD / Hypothyroid / Drug Abuse / PCI / Asthma / GERD / CAD / COPD / HLD / Psych / CKD / Smoker / Dementia / Other :

Tests/Procedures

Neuro	Neuro CIWA	Medical history					Lines
RASS		Meds/VF	Site	Size	Dose	Assessments	IV
NIH		1					CENTRAL
CAM		2					HD
A&O		3					Date
GCS		4					

Cardio/Tele	ACCU-CHECK			Medications
	Time	BS	Cover	
	Time	BS	Cover	
	Time	BS	Cover	

Respiratory		Vitals		GI:	LABS	
	Loungs/02	P	O2	Diet:	NA	WBC
		T	BP	Last BM:	PH	PLT
		R		GU:	K	TROPONIN
					PT/INR	CR
Edema :	Skin :			Mobility :	BUN	CA
Musculoskeletal :					HGB	MG
					OTHER	

Pain Assess :	Pain Reassess :	Blood Sugar :

Fluids:	Output:	Intake:	Notes :
DVT Pophylaxis:			

Plan of Care

Room	Admit Date	Situation	Attending Consult
Name	Allergies		
Age			
Sex	Code		

Hospital course	Present Illness	Precautions
	MD	

PMH : CA / CVA / DM / CHF / HTN / CKD / PVD / ESRD / Hypothyroid / Drug Abuse / PCI / Asthma / GERD / CAD / COPD / HLD / Psych / CKD / Smoker / Dementia / Other :

Tests/Procedures

Neuro	Neuro CIWA	Medical history					Lines
RASS		Meds/VF	Site	Size	Dose	Assessments	IV
NIH		1					CENTRAL
CAM		2					HD
A&O		3					Date
GCS		4					

Cardio/Tele	ACCU-CHECK			Medications
	Time	BS	Cover	
	Time	BS	Cover	
	Time	BS	Cover	

Respiratory	Vitals	GI:	LABS	
Loungs/02	P O2	Diet:	NA	WBC
	T BP	Last BM:	PH	PLT
	R	GU:	K	TROPONIN
			PT/INR	CR
Edema :	Skin :	Mobility :	BUN	CA
Musculoskeletal :			HGB	MG
			OTHER	

Pain Assess :	Pain Reassess :	Blood Sugar :

Fluids:	Output:	Intake:	Notes :
DVT Pophylaxis:			

Plan of Care

45

Room	Admit Date	Situation	Attending Consult
Name	Allergies		
Age			
Sex	Code		

Hospital course	Present Illness	Precautions
	MD	

PMH : CA / CVA / DM / CHF / HTN / CKD / PVD / ESRD / Hypothyroid / Drug Abuse / PCI / Asthma / GERD / CAD / COPD / HLD / Psych / CKD / Smoker / Dementia / Other :

Tests/Procedures

Neuro	Neuro CIWA	Medical history					Lines
RASS		Meds/VF	Site	Size	Dose	Assessments	IV
NIH		1					CENTRAL
CAM		2					HD
A&O		3					Date
GCS		4					

Cardio/Tele	ACCU-CHECK			Medications
	Time	BS	Cover	
	Time	BS	Cover	
	Time	BS	Cover	

Respiratory		Vitals		GI:		LABS	
	Loungs/02	P	O2	Diet:		NA	WBC
		T	BP	Last BM:		PH	PLT
		R		GU:		K	TROPONIN
						PT/INR	CR
Edema :	Skin :			Mobility :		BUN	CA
Musculoskeletal :						HGB	MG
						OTHER	

Pain Assess :	Pain Reassess :	Blood Sugar :

Fluids:	Output:	Intake:	Notes :
DVT Pophylaxis:			

Plan of Care

Room	Admit Date	Situation	Attending Consult
Name	Allergies		
Age			
Sex	Code		

Hospital course	Present Illness	Precautions
	MD	

PMH : CA / CVA / DM / CHF / HTN / CKD / PVD / ESRD / Hypothyroid / Drug Abuse / PCI / Asthma / GERD / CAD / COPD / HLD / Psych / CKD / Smoker / Dementia / Other :

Tests/Procedures

Neuro	Neuro CIWA	Medical history					Lines
RASS		Meds/VF	Site	Size	Dose	Assessments	IV
NIH		1					CENTRAL
CAM		2					HD
A&O		3					Date
GCS		4					

Cardio/Tele	ACCU-CHECK			Medications
	Time	BS	Cover	
	Time	BS	Cover	
	Time	BS	Cover	

Respiratory	Vitals		GI:	LABS	
Loungs/02	P	O2	Diet:	NA	WBC
	T		Last BM:	PH	PLT
		BP	GU:	K	TROPONIN
	R			PT/INR	CR
Edema :	Skin :		Mobility :	BUN	CA
Musculoskeletal :				HGB	MG
				OTHER	

Pain Assess :	Pain Reassess :	Blood Sugar :

Fluids:	Output:	Intake:	Notes :
DVT Pophylaxis:			

Plan of Care

Room	Admit Date	Situation	Attending Consult
Name	Allergies		
Age			
Sex	Code		

Hospital course	Present Illness	Precautions
	MD	

PMH : CA / CVA / DM / CHF / HTN / CKD / PVD / ESRD / Hypothyroid / Drug Abuse / PCI / Asthma / GERD / CAD / COPD / HLD / Psych / CKD / Smoker / Dementia / Other :

Tests/Procedures

Neuro	Neuro CIWA	Medical history					Lines
RASS		Meds/VF	Site	Size	Dose	Assessments	IV
NIH		1					CENTRAL
CAM		2					HD
A&O		3					Date
GCS		4					

Cardio/Tele	ACCU-CHECK			Medications
	Time	BS	Cover	
	Time	BS	Cover	
	Time	BS	Cover	

Respiratory	Vitals		GI:	LABS	
Loungs/02	P	O2	Diet:	NA	WBC
	T		Last BM:	PH	PLT
	R	BP	GU:	K	TROPONIN
				PT/INR	CR
Edema :	Skin :		Mobility :	BUN	CA
Musculoskeletal :				HGB	MG
				OTHER	

Pain Assess :	Pain Reassess :	Blood Sugar :

Fluids:	Output:	Intake:	Notes :
DVT Pophylaxis:			

Plan of Care

Room	Admit Date	Situation	Attending Consult
Name	Allergies		
Age			
Sex	Code		

Hospital course	Present Illness	Precautions
	MD	

PMH : CA / CVA / DM / CHF / HTN / CKD / PVD / ESRD / Hypothyroid / Drug Abuse / PCI / Asthma / GERD / CAD / COPD / HLD / Psych / CKD / Smoker / Dementia / Other :

Tests/Procedures

Neuro	Neuro CIWA	Medical history					Lines
RASS		Meds/VF	Site	Size	Dose	Assessments	IV
NIH		1					CENTRAL
CAM		2					HD
A&O		3					Date
GCS		4					

Cardio/Tele	ACCU-CHECK			Medications
	Time	BS	Cover	
	Time	BS	Cover	
	Time	BS	Cover	

Respiratory	Vitals	GI:	LABS	
Loungs/02	P O2	Diet:	NA	WBC
	T	Last BM:	PH	PLT
	R BP	GU:	K	TROPONIN
			PT/INR	CR
Edema :	Skin :	Mobility :	BUN	CA
Musculoskeletal :			HGB	MG
			OTHER	

Pain Assess :	Pain Reassess :	Blood Sugar :

Fluids:	Output:	Intake:	Notes :
DVT Pophylaxis:			

Plan of Care

Room	Admit Date	Situation	Attending Consult
Name	Allergies		
Age			
Sex	Code		

Hospital course	Present Illness	Precautions
	MD	

PMH : CA / CVA / DM / CHF / HTN / CKD / PVD / ESRD / Hypothyroid / Drug Abuse / PCI / Asthma / GERD / CAD / COPD / HLD / Psych / CKD / Smoker / Dementia / Other :

Tests/Procedures

Neuro	Neuro CIWA	Medical history					Lines
RASS		Meds/VF	Site	Size	Dose	Assessments	IV
NIH		1					CENTRAL
CAM		2					HD
A&O		3					Date
GCS		4					

Cardio/Tele	ACCU-CHECK			Medications
	Time	BS	Cover	
	Time	BS	Cover	
	Time	BS	Cover	

Respiratory		Vitals		GI:	LABS	
	Loungs/02	P	O2	Diet:	NA	WBC
		T	BP	Last BM:	PH	PLT
		R		GU:	K	TROPONIN
					PT/INR	CR

Edema :	Skin :	Mobility :	BUN	CA
Musculoskeletal :			HGB	MG
			OTHER	

Pain Assess :	Pain Reassess :	Blood Sugar :

Fluids:	Output:	Intake:	Notes :

DVT Pophylaxis:

Plan of Care

Room	Admit Date	Situation	Attending Consult
Name	Allergies		
Age			
Sex	Code		

Hospital course	Present Illness	Precautions
	MD	

PMH : CA / CVA / DM / CHF / HTN / CKD / PVD / ESRD / Hypothyroid / Drug Abuse / PCI / Asthma / GERD / CAD / COPD / HLD / Psych / CKD / Smoker / Dementia / Other :

Tests/Procedures

Neuro	Neuro CIWA	Medical history					Lines
RASS		Meds/VF	Site	Size	Dose	Assessments	IV
NIH		1					CENTRAL
CAM		2					HD
A&O		3					Date
GCS		4					

Cardio/Tele	ACCU-CHECK	Medications
	Time BS Cover	
	Time BS Cover	
	Time BS Cover	

Respiratory	Vitals	GI:	LABS	
Loungs/02	P O2	Diet:	NA	WBC
	T BP	Last BM:	PH	PLT
	R	GU:	K	TROPONIN
			PT/INR	CR
Edema :	Skin :	Mobility :	BUN	CA
Musculoskeletal :			HGB	MG
			OTHER	
Pain Assess :	Pain Reassess :	Blood Sugar :		

Fluids:	Output:	Intake:	Notes :
DVT Pophylaxis:			

Plan of Care

Room		Admit Date		Situation		Attending Consult	
Name		Allergies					
Age							
Sex		Code					

Hospital course	Present Illness	Precautions
	MD	

PMH : CA / CVA / DM / CHF / HTN / CKD / PVD / ESRD / Hypothyroid / Drug Abuse / PCI / Asthma / GERD / CAD / COPD / HLD / Psych / CKD / Smoker / Dementia / Other :

Tests/Procedures

Neuro	Neuro CIWA	Medical history					Lines
RASS		Meds/VF	Site	Size	Dose	Assessments	IV
NIH		1					CENTRAL
CAM		2					HD
A&O		3					Date
GCS		4					

Cardio/Tele	ACCU-CHECK			Medications
	Time	BS	Cover	
	Time	BS	Cover	
	Time	BS	Cover	

Respiratory	Vitals	GI:	LABS	
Loungs/02	P O2	Diet:	NA	WBC
	T BP	Last BM:	PH	PLT
	R	GU:	K	TROPONIN
			PT/INR	CR
Edema :	Skin :	Mobility :	BUN	CA
Musculoskeletal :			HGB	MG
			OTHER	

Pain Assess :	Pain Reassess :	Blood Sugar :

Fluids:	Output:	Intake:	Notes :
DVT Pophylaxis:			

Plan of Care

Room	Admit Date	Situation	Attending Consult
Name	Allergies		
Age			
Sex	Code		

Hospital course	Present Illness	Precautions
	MD	

PMH : CA / CVA / DM / CHF / HTN / CKD / PVD / ESRD / Hypothyroid / Drug Abuse / PCI / Asthma / GERD / CAD / COPD / HLD / Psych / CKD / Smoker / Dementia / Other :

Tests/Procedures

Neuro	Neuro CIWA	Medical history					Lines
RASS		Meds/VF	Site	Size	Dose	Assessments	IV
NIH		1					CENTRAL
CAM		2					HD
A&O		3					Date
GCS		4					

Cardio/Tele	ACCU-CHECK			Medications
	Time	BS	Cover	
	Time	BS	Cover	
	Time	BS	Cover	

Respiratory	Vitals	GI:	LABS	
Loungs/02	P	Diet:	NA	WBC
	O2	Last BM:	PH	PLT
	T	GU:	K	TROPONIN
	BP		PT/INR	CR
	R		BUN	CA
Edema :	Skin :	Mobility :	HGB	MG
Musculoskeletal :			OTHER	

Pain Assess :	Pain Reassess :	Blood Sugar :

Fluids:	Output:	Intake:	Notes :

DVT Pophylaxis:

Plan of Care

Room	Admit Date	Situation	Attending Consult
Name	Allergies		
Age			
Sex	Code		

Hospital course	Present Illness	Precautions
	MD	

PMH : CA / CVA / DM / CHF / HTN / CKD / PVD / ESRD / Hypothyroid / Drug Abuse / PCI / Asthma / GERD / CAD / COPD / HLD / Psych / CKD / Smoker / Dementia / Other :

Tests/Procedures

Neuro	Neuro CIWA	Medical history					Lines
RASS		Meds/VF	Site	Size	Dose	Assessments	IV
NIH		1					CENTRAL
CAM		2					HD
A&O		3					Date
GCS		4					

Cardio/Tele	ACCU-CHECK			Medications
	Time	BS	Cover	
	Time	BS	Cover	
	Time	BS	Cover	

Respiratory	Vitals	GI:	LABS	
Loungs/02	P	Diet:	NA	WBC
	T O2	Last BM:	PH	PLT
		GU:	K	TROPONIN
	R BP		PT/INR	CR

Edema :	Skin :	Mobility :	BUN	CA
Musculoskeletal :			HGB	MG
			OTHER	

Pain Assess :	Pain Reassess :	Blood Sugar :	

Fluids:	Output:	Intake:	Notes :

DVT Pophylaxis:

Plan of Care

Room	Admit Date	Situation	Attending Consult
Name	Allergies		
Age			
Sex	Code		

Hospital course	Present Illness	Precautions
	MD	

PMH : CA / CVA / DM / CHF / HTN / CKD / PVD / ESRD / Hypothyroid / Drug Abuse / PCI / Asthma / GERD / CAD / COPD / HLD / Psych / CKD / Smoker / Dementia / Other :

Tests/Procedures

Neuro	Neuro CIWA	Medical history					Lines
RASS		Meds/VF	Site	Size	Dose	Assessments	IV
NIH		1					CENTRAL
CAM		2					HD
A&O		3					Date
GCS		4					

Cardio/Tele	ACCU-CHECK	Medications
	Time BS Cover	
	Time BS Cover	
	Time BS Cover	

Respiratory	Vitals	GI:	LABS	
Loungs/02	P O2	Diet:	NA	WBC
	T BP	Last BM:	PH	PLT
	R	GU:	K	TROPONIN
			PT/INR	CR
Edema :	Skin :	Mobility :	BUN	CA
Musculoskeletal :			HGB	MG
			OTHER	

Pain Assess :	Pain Reassess :	Blood Sugar :

Fluids:	Output:	Intake:	Notes :
DVT Pophylaxis:			

Plan of Care

Room	Admit Date	Situation	Attending Consult
Name	Allergies		
Age			
Sex	Code		

Hospital course	Present Illness	Precautions
	MD	

PMH : CA / CVA / DM / CHF / HTN / CKD / PVD / ESRD / Hypothyroid / Drug Abuse / PCI / Asthma / GERD / CAD / COPD / HLD / Psych / CKD / Smoker / Dementia / Other :

Tests/Procedures

Neuro	Neuro CIWA	Medical history					Lines
RASS		Meds/VF	Site	Size	Dose	Assessments	IV
NIH		1					CENTRAL
CAM		2					HD
A&O		3					Date
GCS		4					

Cardio/Tele	ACCU-CHECK			Medications
	Time	BS	Cover	
	Time	BS	Cover	
	Time	BS	Cover	

Respiratory	Vitals	GI:	LABS	
Loungs/02	P	Diet:	NA	WBC
	O2	Last BM:	PH	PLT
	T	GU:	K	TROPONIN
	BP		PT/INR	CR
	R		BUN	CA

Edema :	Skin :	Mobility :	HGB	MG
Musculoskeletal :			OTHER	

Pain Assess :	Pain Reassess :	Blood Sugar :

Fluids:	Output:	Intake:	Notes :

DVT Pophylaxis:

Plan of Care

Room	Admit Date	Situation	Attending Consult
Name	Allergies		
Age			
Sex	Code		

Hospital course	Present Illness	Precautions
	MD	

PMH : CA / CVA / DM / CHF / HTN / CKD / PVD / ESRD / Hypothyroid / Drug Abuse / PCI / Asthma / GERD / CAD / COPD / HLD / Psych / CKD / Smoker / Dementia / Other :

Tests/Procedures

Neuro	Neuro CIWA	Medical history					Lines
RASS		Meds/VF	Site	Size	Dose	Assessments	IV
NIH		1					CENTRAL
CAM		2					HD
A&O		3					Date
GCS		4					

Cardio/Tele	ACCU-CHECK			Medications
	Time	BS	Cover	
	Time	BS	Cover	
	Time	BS	Cover	

Respiratory	Vitals	GI:	LABS	
Loungs/02	P	Diet:	NA	WBC
	O2	Last BM:	PH	PLT
	T	GU:	K	TROPONIN
	BP		PT/INR	CR
	R		BUN	CA
Edema :	Skin :	Mobility :	HGB	MG
Musculoskeletal :			OTHER	

Pain Assess :	Pain Reassess :	Blood Sugar :	

Fluids:	Output:	Intake:	Notes :
DVT Pophylaxis:			

Plan of Care

Room	Admit Date	Situation	Attending Consult
Name	Allergies		
Age			
Sex	Code		

Hospital course	Present Illness	Precautions
	MD	

PMH : CA / CVA / DM / CHF / HTN / CKD / PVD / ESRD / Hypothyroid / Drug Abuse / PCI / Asthma / GERD / CAD / COPD / HLD / Psych / CKD / Smoker / Dementia / Other :

Tests/Procedures

Neuro	Neuro CIWA	Medical history					Lines
RASS		Meds/VF	Site	Size	Dose	Assessments	IV
NIH		1					CENTRAL
CAM		2					HD
A&O		3					Date
GCS		4					

Cardio/Tele	ACCU-CHECK	Medications
	Time BS Cover	
	Time BS Cover	
	Time BS Cover	

Respiratory	Vitals	GI:	LABS	
Loungs/02	P O2	Diet:	NA	WBC
	T BP	Last BM:	PH	PLT
	R	GU:	K	TROPONIN
			PT/INR	CR

Edema :	Skin :	Mobility :	BUN	CA
			HGB	MG

Musculoskeletal :

OTHER

Pain Assess :	Pain Reassess :	Blood Sugar :

Fluids:	Output:	Intake:	Notes :

DVT Pophylaxis:

Plan of Care

Room	Admit Date	Situation	Attending Consult
Name	Allergies		
Age			
Sex	Code		

Hospital course	Present Illness	Precautions
	MD	

PMH : CA / CVA / DM / CHF / HTN / CKD / PVD / ESRD / Hypothyroid / Drug Abuse / PCI / Asthma / GERD / CAD / COPD / HLD / Psych / CKD / Smoker / Dementia / Other :

Tests/Procedures

Neuro	Neuro CIWA	Medical history					Lines
RASS		Meds/VF	Site	Size	Dose	Assessments	IV
NIH		1					CENTRAL
CAM		2					HD
A&O		3					Date
GCS		4					

Cardio/Tele	ACCU-CHECK			Medications
	Time	BS	Cover	
	Time	BS	Cover	
	Time	BS	Cover	

Respiratory	Vitals	GI:	LABS	
Loungs/02	P	Diet:	NA	WBC
	O2	Last BM:	PH	PLT
	T	GU:	K	TROPONIN
	BP		PT/INR	CR
	R			

Edema :	Skin :	Mobility :	BUN	CA
Musculoskeletal :			HGB	MG
			OTHER	

Pain Assess :	Pain Reassess :	Blood Sugar :

Fluids:	Output:	Intake:	Notes :
DVT Pophylaxis:			

Plan of Care

Room	Admit Date	Situation	Attending Consult
Name	Allergies		
Age			
Sex	Code		

Hospital course	Present Illness	Precautions
	MD	

PMH : CA / CVA / DM / CHF / HTN / CKD / PVD / ESRD / Hypothyroid / Drug Abuse / PCI / Asthma / GERD / CAD
/ COPD / HLD / Psych / CKD / Smoker / Dementia / Other :

Tests/Procedures

Neuro	Neuro CIWA	Medical history					Lines
RASS		Meds/VF	Site	Size	Dose	Assessments	IV
NIH		1					CENTRAL
CAM		2					HD
A&O		3					Date
GCS		4					

Cardio/Tele	ACCU-CHECK			Medications
	Time	BS	Cover	
	Time	BS	Cover	
	Time	BS	Cover	

Respiratory	Vitals	GI:	LABS	
Loungs/02	P	Diet:	NA	WBC
	O2	Last BM:	PH	PLT
	T	GU:	K	TROPONIN
	BP		PT/INR	CR
	R		BUN	CA

Edema :	Skin :	Mobility :	HGB	MG

Musculoskeletal :

OTHER

Pain Assess :	Pain Reassess :	Blood Sugar :

Fluids:	Output:	Intake:	Notes :

DVT Pophylaxis:

Plan of Care

Room	Admit Date	Situation	Attending Consult
Name	Allergies		
Age			
Sex	Code		

Hospital course	Present Illness	Precautions
	MD	

PMH : CA / CVA / DM / CHF / HTN / CKD / PVD / ESRD / Hypothyroid / Drug Abuse / PCI / Asthma / GERD / CAD / COPD / HLD / Psych / CKD / Smoker / Dementia / Other :

Tests/Procedures

Neuro	Neuro CIWA	Medical history					Lines
RASS		Meds/VF	Site	Size	Dose	Assessments	IV
NIH		1					CENTRAL
CAM		2					HD
A&O		3					Date
GCS		4					

Cardio/Tele	ACCU-CHECK			Medications
	Time	BS	Cover	
	Time	BS	Cover	
	Time	BS	Cover	

Respiratory	Vitals	GI:	LABS	
Loungs/02	P O2	Diet:	NA	WBC
	T	Last BM:	PH	PLT
	R BP	GU:	K	TROPONIN
			PT/INR	CR
Edema :	Skin :	Mobility :	BUN	CA
			HGB	MG
Musculoskeletal :			OTHER	

Pain Assess :	Pain Reassess :	Blood Sugar :

Fluids:	Output:	Intake:	Notes :
DVT Pophylaxis:			

Plan of Care

Room	Admit Date	Situation	Attending Consult
Name	**Allergies**		
Age			
Sex	**Code**		

Hospital course	Present Illness	Precautions
	MD	

PMH : CA / CVA / DM / CHF / HTN / CKD / PVD / ESRD / Hypothyroid / Drug Abuse / PCI / Asthma / GERD / CAD / COPD / HLD / Psych / CKD / Smoker / Dementia / Other :

Tests/Procedures

Neuro	Neuro CIWA	Medical history					Lines
RASS		Meds/VF	Site	Size	Dose	Assessments	IV
NIH		1					CENTRAL
CAM		2					HD
A&O		3					Date
GCS		4					

Cardio/Tele	ACCU-CHECK	Medications
	Time BS Cover	
	Time BS Cover	
	Time BS Cover	

Respiratory	Vitals	GI:	LABS	
Loungs/02	P O2	Diet:	NA	WBC
	T BP	Last BM:	PH	PLT
	R	GU:	K	TROPONIN
			PT/INR	CR
Edema :	**Skin :**	**Mobility :**	BUN	CA
			HGB	MG
Musculoskeletal :			OTHER	

Pain Assess :	Pain Reassess :	Blood Sugar :

Fluids:	Output:	Intake:	Notes :

DVT Pophylaxis:

Plan of Care

Room	Admit Date	Situation	Attending Consult
Name	Allergies		
Age			
Sex	Code		

Hospital course	Present Illness	Precautions
	MD	

PMH : CA / CVA / DM / CHF / HTN / CKD / PVD / ESRD / Hypothyroid / Drug Abuse / PCI / Asthma / GERD / CAD / COPD / HLD / Psych / CKD / Smoker / Dementia / Other :

Tests/Procedures

Neuro	Neuro CIWA	Medical history					Lines
RASS		Meds/VF	Site	Size	Dose	Assessments	IV
NIH		1					CENTRAL
CAM		2					HD
A&O		3					Date
GCS		4					

Cardio/Tele	ACCU-CHECK			Medications
	Time	BS	Cover	
	Time	BS	Cover	
	Time	BS	Cover	

Respiratory	Vitals		GI:	LABS	
Loungs/02	P	O2	Diet:	NA	WBC
	T	BP	Last BM:	PH	PLT
	R		GU:	K	TROPONIN
				PT/INR	CR
Edema :	Skin :		Mobility :	BUN	CA
Musculoskeletal :				HGB	MG
				OTHER	

Pain Assess :	Pain Reassess :	Blood Sugar :

Fluids:	Output:	Intake:	Notes :
DVT Pophylaxis:			

Plan of Care

Room	Admit Date	Situation	Attending Consult
Name	Allergies		
Age			
Sex	Code		

Hospital course	Present Illness	Precautions
	MD	

PMH : CA / CVA / DM / CHF / HTN / CKD / PVD / ESRD / Hypothyroid / Drug Abuse / PCI / Asthma / GERD / CAD / COPD / HLD / Psych / CKD / Smoker / Dementia / Other :

Tests/Procedures

Neuro	Neuro CIWA	Medical history					Lines
RASS		Meds/VF	Site	Size	Dose	Assessments	IV
NIH		1					CENTRAL
CAM		2					HD
A&O		3					Date
GCS		4					

Cardio/Tele	ACCU-CHECK			Medications
	Time	BS	Cover	
	Time	BS	Cover	
	Time	BS	Cover	

Respiratory	Vitals		GI:	LABS	
Loungs/02	P	O2	Diet:	NA	WBC
	T	BP	Last BM:	PH	PLT
	R		GU:	K	TROPONIN
				PT/INR	CR
Edema :	Skin :		Mobility :	BUN	CA
Musculoskeletal :				HGB	MG
				OTHER	

Pain Assess :	Pain Reassess :	Blood Sugar :

Fluids:	Output:	Intake:	Notes :

DVT Pophylaxis:	

Plan of Care

Room	Admit Date	Situation	Attending Consult
Name	Allergies		
Age			
Sex	Code		

Hospital course	Present Illness	Precautions
	MD	

PMH : CA / CVA / DM / CHF / HTN / CKD / PVD / ESRD / Hypothyroid / Drug Abuse / PCI / Asthma / GERD / CAD / COPD / HLD / Psych / CKD / Smoker / Dementia / Other :

Tests/Procedures

Neuro	Neuro CIWA	Medical history					Lines
RASS		Meds/VF	Site	Size	Dose	Assessments	IV
NIH		1					CENTRAL
CAM		2					HD
A&O		3					Date
GCS		4					

Cardio/Tele	ACCU-CHECK			Medications
	Time	BS	Cover	
	Time	BS	Cover	
	Time	BS	Cover	

Respiratory	Vitals		GI:	LABS	
Loungs/02	P O2		Diet:	NA	WBC
			Last BM:	PH	PLT
	T BP		GU:	K	TROPONIN
	R			PT/INR	CR
Edema :	Skin :		Mobility :	BUN	CA
Musculoskeletal :				HGB	MG
				OTHER	

Pain Assess :	Pain Reassess :	Blood Sugar :

Fluids:	Output:	Intake:	Notes :
DVT Pophylaxis:			

Plan of Care

Room	Admit Date	Situation	Attending Consult
Name	Allergies		
Age			
Sex	Code		

Hospital course	Present Illness	Precautions
	MD	

PMH : CA / CVA / DM / CHF / HTN / CKD / PVD / ESRD / Hypothyroid / Drug Abuse / PCI / Asthma / GERD / CAD / COPD / HLD / Psych / CKD / Smoker / Dementia / Other :

Tests/Procedures

Neuro	Neuro CIWA	Medical history					Lines
RASS		Meds/VF	Site	Size	Dose	Assessments	IV
NIH		1					CENTRAL
CAM		2					HD
A&O		3					Date
GCS		4					

Cardio/Tele	ACCU-CHECK			Medications
	Time	BS	Cover	
	Time	BS	Cover	
	Time	BS	Cover	

Respiratory	Vitals		GI:	LABS	
Loungs/02	P	O2	Diet:	NA	WBC
	T		Last BM:	PH	PLT
		BP	GU:	K	TROPONIN
	R			PT/INR	CR
Edema :	Skin :		Mobility :	BUN	CA
Musculoskeletal :				HGB	MG
				OTHER	

Pain Assess :	Pain Reassess :	Blood Sugar :

Fluids:	Output:	Intake:	Notes :
DVT Pophylaxis:			

Plan of Care

Room	Admit Date	Situation	Attending Consult
Name	Allergies		
Age			
Sex	Code		

Hospital course	Present Illness	Precautions
	MD	

PMH : CA / CVA / DM / CHF / HTN / CKD / PVD / ESRD / Hypothyroid / Drug Abuse / PCI / Asthma / GERD / CAD / COPD / HLD / Psych / CKD / Smoker / Dementia / Other :

Tests/Procedures

Neuro	Neuro CIWA	Medical history					Lines
RASS		Meds/VF	Site	Size	Dose	Assessments	IV
NIH		1					CENTRAL
CAM		2					HD
A&O		3					Date
GCS		4					

Cardio/Tele	ACCU-CHECK			Medications
	Time	BS	Cover	
	Time	BS	Cover	
	Time	BS	Cover	

Respiratory	Vitals	GI:	LABS	
Loungs/02	P	Diet:	NA	WBC
		O2		PH	PLT
	T		Last BM:	K	TROPONIN
		BP	GU:	PT/INR	CR
	R			BUN	CA

Edema :	Skin :	Mobility :	HGB	MG
Musculoskeletal :			OTHER	

Pain Assess :	Pain Reassess :	Blood Sugar :

Fluids:	Output:	Intake:	Notes :

DVT Pophylaxis:

Plan of Care

Room	Admit Date	Situation	Attending Consult
Name	**Allergies**		
Age			
Sex	**Code**		

Hospital course	Present Illness	Precautions
	MD	

PMH : CA / CVA / DM / CHF / HTN / CKD / PVD / ESRD / Hypothyroid / Drug Abuse / PCI / Asthma / GERD / CAD / COPD / HLD / Psych / CKD / Smoker / Dementia / Other :

Tests/Procedures

Neuro	Neuro CIWA	Medical history					Lines
RASS		Meds/VF	Site	Size	Dose	Assessments	IV
NIH		1					CENTRAL
CAM		2					HD
A&O		3					Date
GCS		4					

Cardio/Tele	ACCU-CHECK	Medications
	Time BS Cover	
	Time BS Cover	
	Time BS Cover	

Respiratory	Vitals	GI:	LABS	
Loungs/02	P O2	Diet:	NA	WBC
	T BP	Last BM:	PH	PLT
	R	GU:	K	TROPONIN
			PT/INR	CR
Edema :	**Skin :**	**Mobility :**	BUN	CA
Musculoskeletal :			HGB	MG
			OTHER	

Pain Assess :	Pain Reassess :	Blood Sugar :

Fluids:	Output:	Intake:	Notes :

DVT Pophylaxis:

Plan of Care

68

Room	Admit Date	Situation	Attending Consult
Name	Allergies		
Age			
Sex	Code		

Hospital course	Present Illness	Precautions
	MD	

PMH : CA / CVA / DM / CHF / HTN / CKD / PVD / ESRD / Hypothyroid / Drug Abuse / PCI / Asthma / GERD / CAD / COPD / HLD / Psych / CKD / Smoker / Dementia / Other :

Tests/Procedures

Neuro	Neuro CIWA	Medical history					Lines
RASS		Meds/VF	Site	Size	Dose	Assessments	IV
NIH		1					CENTRAL
CAM		2					HD
A&O		3					Date
GCS		4					

Cardio/Tele	ACCU-CHECK			Medications
	Time	BS	Cover	
	Time	BS	Cover	
	Time	BS	Cover	

Respiratory	Vitals	GI:	LABS	
Loungs/02	P O2	Diet:	NA	WBC
	T BP	Last BM:	PH	PLT
	R	GU:	K	TROPONIN
			PT/INR	CR
Edema :	Skin :	Mobility :	BUN	CA
Musculoskeletal :			HGB	MG
			OTHER	

Pain Assess :	Pain Reassess :	Blood Sugar :

Fluids:	Output:	Intake:	Notes :
DVT Pophylaxis:			

Plan of Care

Room	Admit Date	Situation	Attending Consult
Name	Allergies		
Age			
Sex	Code		

Hospital course	Present Illness	Precautions
	MD	

PMH : CA / CVA / DM / CHF / HTN / CKD / PVD / ESRD / Hypothyroid / Drug Abuse / PCI / Asthma / GERD / CAD / COPD / HLD / Psych / CKD / Smoker / Dementia / Other :

Tests/Procedures

Neuro	Neuro CIWA	Medical history					Lines
RASS		Meds/VF	Site	Size	Dose	Assessments	IV
NIH		1					CENTRAL
CAM		2					HD
A&O		3					Date
GCS		4					

Cardio/Tele	ACCU-CHECK			Medications
	Time	BS	Cover	
	Time	BS	Cover	
	Time	BS	Cover	

Respiratory	Vitals	GI:	LABS	
Loungs/02	P / O2 / T / BP / R	Diet: / Last BM: / GU:	NA	WBC
			PH	PLT
			K	TROPONIN
			PT/INR	CR
Edema :	Skin :	Mobility :	BUN	CA
Musculoskeletal :			HGB	MG
			OTHER	

Pain Assess :	Pain Reassess :	Blood Sugar :

Fluids:	Output:	Intake:	Notes :

DVT Pophylaxis:

Plan of Care

Room	Admit Date	Situation	Attending Consult
Name	Allergies		
Age			
Sex	Code		

Hospital course	Present Illness	Precautions
	MD	

PMH : CA / CVA / DM / CHF / HTN / CKD / PVD / ESRD / Hypothyroid / Drug Abuse / PCI / Asthma / GERD / CAD / COPD / HLD / Psych / CKD / Smoker / Dementia / Other :

Tests/Procedures

Neuro	Neuro CIWA	Medical history					Lines
RASS		Meds/VF	Site	Size	Dose	Assessments	IV
NIH		1					CENTRAL
CAM		2					HD
A&O		3					Date
GCS		4					

Cardio/Tele	ACCU-CHECK			Medications
	Time	BS	Cover	
	Time	BS	Cover	
	Time	BS	Cover	

Respiratory	Vitals	GI:	LABS	
Loungs/02	P O2	Diet:	NA	WBC
	T BP	Last BM:	PH	PLT
	R	GU:	K	TROPONIN
			PT/INR	CR
Edema :	Skin :	Mobility :	BUN	CA
Musculoskeletal :			HGB	MG
			OTHER	

Pain Assess :	Pain Reassess :	Blood Sugar :

Fluids:	Output:	Intake:	Notes :
DVT Pophylaxis:			

Plan of Care

Room	Admit Date	Situation	Attending Consult
Name	Allergies		
Age			
Sex	Code		

Hospital course	Present Illness	Precautions
	MD	

PMH : CA / CVA / DM / CHF / HTN / CKD / PVD / ESRD / Hypothyroid / Drug Abuse / PCI / Asthma / GERD / CAD / COPD / HLD / Psych / CKD / Smoker / Dementia / Other :

Tests/Procedures

Neuro	Neuro CIWA		Medical history					Lines
RASS			Meds/VF	Site	Size	Dose	Assessments	IV
NIH			1					CENTRAL
CAM			2					HD
A&O			3					Date
GCS			4					

Cardio/Tele	ACCU-CHECK			Medications
	Time	BS	Cover	
	Time	BS	Cover	
	Time	BS	Cover	

Respiratory		Vitals		GI:		LABS	
Loungs/02		P	O2	Diet:		NA	WBC
		T	BP	Last BM:		PH	PLT
		R		GU:		K	TROPONIN
						PT/INR	CR
Edema :	Skin :			Mobility :		BUN	CA
Musculoskeletal :						HGB	MG
						OTHER	

Pain Assess :	Pain Reassess :	Blood Sugar :

Fluids:	Output:	Intake:	Notes :
DVT Pophylaxis:			

Plan of Care

Room	Admit Date	Situation	Attending Consult
Name	**Allergies**		
Age			
Sex	**Code**		

Hospital course	Present Illness	Precautions
	MD	

PMH : CA / CVA / DM / CHF / HTN / CKD / PVD / ESRD / Hypothyroid / Drug Abuse / PCI / Asthma / GERD / CAD / COPD / HLD / Psych / CKD / Smoker / Dementia / Other :

Tests/Procedures

Neuro	Neuro CIWA	Medical history					Lines
RASS		Meds/VF	Site	Size	Dose	Assessments	IV
NIH		1					CENTRAL
CAM		2					HD
A&O		3					Date
GCS		4					

Cardio/Tele	ACCU-CHECK			Medications
	Time	BS	Cover	
	Time	BS	Cover	
	Time	BS	Cover	

Respiratory	Vitals	GI:	LABS	
Loungs/02	P O2	Diet:	NA	WBC
	T BP	Last BM:	PH	PLT
	R	GU:	K	TROPONIN
			PT/INR	CR
Edema : **Skin :** **Mobility :**			BUN	CA
Musculoskeletal :			HGB	MG
			OTHER	

Pain Assess :	Pain Reassess :	Blood Sugar :

Fluids:	Output:	Intake:	Notes :

DVT Pophylaxis:

Plan of Care

Room	Admit Date	Situation	Attending Consult
Name	Allergies		
Age			
Sex	Code		

Hospital course	Present Illness	Precautions
	MD	

PMH : CA / CVA / DM / CHF / HTN / CKD / PVD / ESRD / Hypothyroid / Drug Abuse / PCI / Asthma / GERD / CAD / COPD / HLD / Psych / CKD / Smoker / Dementia / Other :

Tests/Procedures

Neuro	Neuro CIWA	Medical history					Lines
RASS		Meds/VF	Site	Size	Dose	Assessments	IV
NIH		1					CENTRAL
CAM		2					HD
A&O		3					Date
GCS		4					

Cardio/Tele	ACCU-CHECK			Medications
	Time	BS	Cover	
	Time	BS	Cover	
	Time	BS	Cover	

Respiratory	Vitals		GI:	LABS	
Loungs/02	P		Diet:	NA	WBC
		O2	Last BM:	PH	PLT
	T		GU:	K	TROPONIN
		BP		PT/INR	CR
	R			BUN	CA

Edema :	Skin :	Mobility :	HGB	MG
Musculoskeletal :			OTHER	

Pain Assess :	Pain Reassess :	Blood Sugar :

Fluids:	Output:	Intake:	Notes :
DVT Pophylaxis:			

Plan of Care

Room	Admit Date	Situation	Attending Consult
Name	**Allergies**		
Age			
Sex	**Code**		

Hospital course	Present Illness	Precautions
	MD	

PMH : CA / CVA / DM / CHF / HTN / CKD / PVD / ESRD / Hypothyroid / Drug Abuse / PCI / Asthma / GERD / CAD / COPD / HLD / Psych / CKD / Smoker / Dementia / Other :

Tests/Procedures

Neuro	Neuro CIWA	Medical history					Lines
RASS		Meds/VF	Site	Size	Dose	Assessments	IV
NIH		1					CENTRAL
CAM		2					HD
A&O		3					Date
GCS		4					

Cardio/Tele	ACCU-CHECK			Medications
	Time	BS	Cover	
	Time	BS	Cover	
	Time	BS	Cover	

Respiratory	Vitals		GI:	LABS	
Loungs/02	P	O2	Diet:	NA	WBC
	T	BP	Last BM:	PH	PLT
	R		GU:	K	TROPONIN
				PT/INR	CR
Edema :	**Skin :**		**Mobility :**	BUN	CA
Musculoskeletal :				HGB	MG
				OTHER	

Pain Assess :	Pain Reassess :	Blood Sugar :

Fluids:	Output:	Intake:	Notes :

DVT Pophylaxis:

Plan of Care

Room	Admit Date	Situation	Attending Consult
Name	Allergies		
Age			
Sex	Code		

Hospital course	Present Illness	Precautions
	MD	

PMH : CA / CVA / DM / CHF / HTN / CKD / PVD / ESRD / Hypothyroid / Drug Abuse / PCI / Asthma / GERD / CAD / COPD / HLD / Psych / CKD / Smoker / Dementia / Other :

Tests/Procedures

Neuro	Neuro CIWA	Medical history					Lines
RASS		Meds/VF	Site	Size	Dose	Assessments	IV
NIH		1					CENTRAL
CAM		2					HD
A&O		3					Date
GCS		4					

Cardio/Tele	ACCU-CHECK			Medications
	Time	BS	Cover	
	Time	BS	Cover	
	Time	BS	Cover	

Respiratory	Vitals		GI:	LABS	
Loungs/02	P		Diet:	NA	WBC
		O2	Last BM:	PH	PLT
	T		GU:	K	TROPONIN
		BP		PT/INR	CR
	R			BUN	CA
Edema :	Skin :		Mobility :	HGB	MG
Musculoskeletal :				OTHER	

Pain Assess :	Pain Reassess :	Blood Sugar :

Fluids:	Output:	Intake:	Notes :
DVT Pophylaxis:			

Plan of Care

Room	Admit Date	Situation	Attending Consult
Name	Allergies		
Age			
Sex	Code		

Hospital course	Present Illness	Precautions
	MD	

PMH : CA / CVA / DM / CHF / HTN / CKD / PVD / ESRD / Hypothyroid / Drug Abuse / PCI / Asthma / GERD / CAD / COPD / HLD / Psych / CKD / Smoker / Dementia / Other :

Tests/Procedures

Neuro	Neuro CIWA	Medical history					Lines
RASS		Meds/VF	Site	Size	Dose	Assessments	IV
NIH		1					CENTRAL
CAM		2					HD
A&O		3					Date
GCS		4					

Cardio/Tele	ACCU-CHECK			Medications
	Time	BS	Cover	
	Time	BS	Cover	
	Time	BS	Cover	

Respiratory	Vitals	GI:	LABS	
Loungs/02	P	Diet:	NA	WBC
		O2	Last BM:	PH	PLT
	T		BP	GU:	K	TROPONIN
	R			PT/INR	CR

Edema :	Skin :	Mobility :	BUN	CA
Musculoskeletal :			HGB	MG
			OTHER	

Pain Assess :	Pain Reassess :	Blood Sugar :

Fluids:	Output:	Intake:	Notes :
DVT Pophylaxis:			

Plan of Care

Room	Admit Date	Situation	Attending Consult
Name	Allergies		
Age			
Sex	Code		

Hospital course	Present Illness	Precautions
	MD	

PMH : CA / CVA / DM / CHF / HTN / CKD / PVD / ESRD / Hypothyroid / Drug Abuse / PCI / Asthma / GERD / CAD / COPD / HLD / Psych / CKD / Smoker / Dementia / Other :

Tests/Procedures

Neuro	Neuro CIWA		Medical history				Lines
RASS		Meds/VF	Site	Size	Dose	Assessments	IV
NIH							CENTRAL
CAM		1					HD
A&O		2					Date
GCS		3					
		4					

Cardio/Tele	ACCU-CHECK			Medications
	Time	BS	Cover	
	Time	BS	Cover	
	Time	BS	Cover	

Respiratory		Vitals		GI:		LABS	
	Loungs/02	P		Diet:	NA		WBC
			O2	Last BM:	PH		PLT
		T		GU:	K		TROPONIN
			BP		PT/INR		CR
		R			BUN		CA
Edema :		Skin :		Mobility :	HGB		MG
Musculoskeletal :					OTHER		

Pain Assess :	Pain Reassess :	Blood Sugar :

Fluids:	Output:	Intake:	Notes :
DVT Pophylaxis:			

Plan of Care

Room	Admit Date	Situation	Attending Consult
Name	Allergies		
Age			
Sex	Code		

Hospital course	Present Illness	Precautions
	MD	

PMH : CA / CVA / DM / CHF / HTN / CKD / PVD / ESRD / Hypothyroid / Drug Abuse / PCI / Asthma / GERD / CAD / COPD / HLD / Psych / CKD / Smoker / Dementia / Other :

Tests/Procedures

Neuro	Neuro CIWA	Medical history					Lines
RASS		Meds/VF	Site	Size	Dose	Assessments	IV
NIH		1					CENTRAL
CAM		2					HD
A&O		3					Date
GCS		4					

Cardio/Tele	ACCU-CHECK	Medications
	Time BS Cover	
	Time BS Cover	
	Time BS Cover	

Respiratory	Vitals	GI:	LABS	
Loungs/02	P O2	Diet:	NA	WBC
	T BP	Last BM:	PH	PLT
	R	GU:	K	TROPONIN
			PT/INR	CR
Edema :	Skin :	Mobility :	BUN	CA
Musculoskeletal :			HGB	MG
			OTHER	

Pain Assess :	Pain Reassess :	Blood Sugar :	

Fluids:	Output:	Intake:	Notes :
DVT Pophylaxis:			

Plan of Care

Room	Admit Date	Situation	Attending Consult
Name	Allergies		
Age			
Sex	Code		

Hospital course	Present Illness	Precautions
	MD	

PMH : CA / CVA / DM / CHF / HTN / CKD / PVD / ESRD / Hypothyroid / Drug Abuse / PCI / Asthma / GERD / CAD / COPD / HLD / Psych / CKD / Smoker / Dementia / Other :

Tests/Procedures

Neuro	Neuro CIWA	Medical history					Lines
RASS		Meds/VF	Site	Size	Dose	Assessments	IV
NIH		1					CENTRAL
CAM		2					HD
A&O		3					Date
GCS		4					

Cardio/Tele	ACCU-CHECK			Medications
	Time	BS	Cover	
	Time	BS	Cover	
	Time	BS	Cover	

Respiratory	Vitals		GI:	LABS	
Loungs/02	P		Diet:	NA	WBC
		O2		PH	PLT
	T		Last BM:	K	TROPONIN
		BP	GU:	PT/INR	CR
	R			BUN	CA
Edema :	Skin :		Mobility :	HGB	MG
Musculoskeletal :				OTHER	

Pain Assess :	Pain Reassess :	Blood Sugar :

Fluids:	Output:	Intake:	Notes :
DVT Pophylaxis:			

Plan of Care

Room	Admit Date	Situation	Attending Consult
Name	Allergies		
Age			
Sex	Code		

Hospital course	Present Illness	Precautions
	MD	

PMH : CA / CVA / DM / CHF / HTN / CKD / PVD / ESRD / Hypothyroid / Drug Abuse / PCI / Asthma / GERD / CAD / COPD / HLD / Psych / CKD / Smoker / Dementia / Other :

Tests/Procedures

Neuro	Neuro CIWA	Medical history					Lines
RASS		Meds/VF	Site	Size	Dose	Assessments	IV
NIH		1					CENTRAL
CAM		2					HD
A&O		3					Date
GCS		4					

Cardio/Tele	ACCU-CHECK	Medications
	Time　　BS　　Cover	
	Time　　BS　　Cover	
	Time　　BS　　Cover	

Respiratory	Vitals	GI:	LABS	
Loungs/02	P　　　　O2	Diet:	NA	WBC
	T　　　　BP	Last BM:	PH	PLT
	R	GU:	K	TROPONIN
			PT/INR	CR
Edema :	Skin :	Mobility :	BUN	CA
Musculoskeletal :			HGB	MG
			OTHER	

Pain Assess :	Pain Reassess :	Blood Sugar :

Fluids:	Output:	Intake:	Notes :
DVT Pophylaxis:			

Plan of Care

Room	Admit Date	Situation	Attending Consult
Name	Allergies		
Age			
Sex	Code		

Hospital course	Present Illness	Precautions
	MD	

PMH : CA / CVA / DM / CHF / HTN / CKD / PVD / ESRD / Hypothyroid / Drug Abuse / PCI / Asthma / GERD / CAD / COPD / HLD / Psych / CKD / Smoker / Dementia / Other :

Tests/Procedures

Neuro	Neuro CIWA	Medical history					Lines
RASS		Meds/VF	Site	Size	Dose	Assessments	IV
NIH		1					CENTRAL
CAM		2					HD
A&O		3					Date
GCS		4					

Cardio/Tele	ACCU-CHECK	Medications
	Time BS Cover	
	Time BS Cover	
	Time BS Cover	

Respiratory	Vitals	GI:	LABS	
Loungs/02	P O2	Diet:	NA	WBC
	T BP	Last BM:	PH	PLT
	R	GU:	K	TROPONIN
			PT/INR	CR
Edema : Skin :		Mobility :	BUN	CA
Musculoskeletal :			HGB	MG
			OTHER	

Pain Assess :	Pain Reassess :	Blood Sugar :

Fluids:	Output:	Intake:	Notes :

DVT Pophylaxis:

Plan of Care

Room	Admit Date	Situation	Attending Consult
Name	**Allergies**		
Age			
Sex	**Code**		

Hospital course	Present Illness	Precautions
	MD	

PMH : CA / CVA / DM / CHF / HTN / CKD / PVD / ESRD / Hypothyroid / Drug Abuse / PCI / Asthma / GERD / CAD / COPD / HLD / Psych / CKD / Smoker / Dementia / Other :

Tests/Procedures

Neuro	Neuro CIWA						Lines
		Medical history					
RASS		Meds/VF	Site	Size	Dose	Assessments	IV
NIH		1					CENTRAL
CAM		2					HD
A&O		3					Date
GCS		4					

Cardio/Tele	ACCU-CHECK			Medications
	Time	BS	Cover	
	Time	BS	Cover	
	Time	BS	Cover	

Respiratory	Vitals	GI:	LABS	
Loungs/02	P	Diet:	NA	WBC
	O2	Last BM:	PH	PLT
	T	GU:	K	TROPONIN
	BP		PT/INR	CR
	R			

Edema :	Skin :	Mobility :	BUN	CA
Musculoskeletal :			HGB	MG
			OTHER	

Pain Assess :	Pain Reassess :	Blood Sugar :

Fluids:	Output:	Intake:	Notes :
DVT Pophylaxis:			

Plan of Care

Room	Admit Date	Situation	Attending Consult
Name	Allergies		
Age			
Sex	Code		

Hospital course	Present Illness	Precautions
	MD	

PMH : CA / CVA / DM / CHF / HTN / CKD / PVD / ESRD / Hypothyroid / Drug Abuse / PCI / Asthma / GERD / CAD / COPD / HLD / Psych / CKD / Smoker / Dementia / Other :

Tests/Procedures

Neuro	Neuro CIWA	Medical history					Lines
RASS		Meds/VF	Site	Size	Dose	Assessments	IV
NIH		1					CENTRAL
CAM		2					HD
A&O		3					Date
GCS		4					

Cardio/Tele	ACCU-CHECK	Medications
	Time BS Cover	
	Time BS Cover	
	Time BS Cover	

Respiratory	Vitals	GI:	LABS	
Loungs/02	P O2	Diet:	NA	WBC
	T BP	Last BM:	PH	PLT
	R	GU:	K	TROPONIN
			PT/INR	CR
Edema :	Skin :	Mobility :	BUN	CA
Musculoskeletal :			HGB	MG
			OTHER	

Pain Assess :	Pain Reassess :	Blood Sugar :

Fluids:	Output:	Intake:	Notes :

DVT Pophylaxis:

Plan of Care

Room		Admit Date		Situation		Attending Consult	
Name		Allergies					
Age							
Sex		Code					

Hospital course	Present Illness	Precautions
	MD	

PMH : CA / CVA / DM / CHF / HTN / CKD / PVD / ESRD / Hypothyroid / Drug Abuse / PCI / Asthma / GERD / CAD / COPD / HLD / Psych / CKD / Smoker / Dementia / Other :

Tests/Procedures

Neuro	Neuro CIWA	Medical history					Lines
RASS		Meds/VF	Site	Size	Dose	Assessments	IV
NIH		1					CENTRAL
CAM		2					HD
A&O		3					Date
GCS		4					

Cardio/Tele	ACCU-CHECK			Medications
	Time	BS	Cover	
	Time	BS	Cover	
	Time	BS	Cover	

Respiratory	Vitals		GI:	LABS	
Loungs/02	P	O2	Diet:	NA	WBC
	T	BP	Last BM:	PH	PLT
	R		GU:	K	TROPONIN
				PT/INR	CR
Edema :	Skin :		Mobility :	BUN	CA
Musculoskeletal :				HGB	MG
				OTHER	

Pain Assess :	Pain Reassess :	Blood Sugar :	

Fluids:	Output:	Intake:	Notes :
DVT Pophylaxis:			

Plan of Care

Room	Admit Date	Situation	Attending Consult
Name	**Allergies**		
Age			
Sex	**Code**		

Hospital course	Present Illness	Precautions
	MD	

PMH : CA / CVA / DM / CHF / HTN / CKD / PVD / ESRD / Hypothyroid / Drug Abuse / PCI / Asthma / GERD / CAD / COPD / HLD / Psych / CKD / Smoker / Dementia / Other :

Tests/Procedures

Neuro	Neuro CIWA	Medical history					Lines
RASS			Meds/VF	Site	Size	Dose	Assessments	IV
NIH		1					CENTRAL
CAM		2					HD
A&O		3					Date
GCS		4					

Cardio/Tele	ACCU-CHECK	Medications
	Time BS Cover	
	Time BS Cover	
	Time BS Cover	

Respiratory	Vitals	GI:	LABS	
Loungs/02	P O2 T BP R	Diet: Last BM: GU:	NA	WBC
			PH	PLT
			K	TROPONIN
			PT/INR	CR

Edema :	Skin :	Mobility :	BUN	CA
Musculoskeletal :			HGB	MG
			OTHER	

Pain Assess :	Pain Reassess :	Blood Sugar :

Fluids:	Output:	Intake:	Notes :

DVT Pophylaxis:

Plan of Care

Room	Admit Date	Situation	Attending Consult
Name	Allergies		
Age			
Sex	Code		

Hospital course	Present Illness	Precautions
	MD	

PMH : CA / CVA / DM / CHF / HTN / CKD / PVD / ESRD / Hypothyroid / Drug Abuse / PCI / Asthma / GERD / CAD / COPD / HLD / Psych / CKD / Smoker / Dementia / Other :

Tests/Procedures

Neuro	Neuro CIWA	Medical history					Lines
RASS		Meds/VF	Site	Size	Dose	Assessments	IV
NIH		1					CENTRAL
CAM		2					HD
A&O		3					Date
GCS		4					

Cardio/Tele	ACCU-CHECK			Medications
	Time	BS	Cover	
	Time	BS	Cover	
	Time	BS	Cover	

Respiratory	Vitals	GI:	LABS	
Loungs/02	P O2	Diet:	NA	WBC
	T BP	Last BM:	PH	PLT
	R	GU:	K	TROPONIN
			PT/INR	CR
Edema : Skin :		Mobility :	BUN	CA
Musculoskeletal :			HGB	MG
			OTHER	

Pain Assess :	Pain Reassess :	Blood Sugar :

Fluids:	Output:	Intake:	Notes :
DVT Pophylaxis:			

Plan of Care

Room	Admit Date	Situation	Attending Consult
Name	**Allergies**		
Age			
Sex	**Code**		

Hospital course	Present Illness	Precautions
	MD	

PMH : CA / CVA / DM / CHF / HTN / CKD / PVD / ESRD / Hypothyroid / Drug Abuse / PCI / Asthma / GERD / CAD / COPD / HLD / Psych / CKD / Smoker / Dementia / Other :

Tests/Procedures

Neuro	Neuro CIWA	Medical history					Lines
RASS		Meds/VF	Site	Size	Dose	Assessments	IV
NIH		1					CENTRAL
CAM		2					HD
A&O		3					Date
GCS		4					

Cardio/Tele	ACCU-CHECK			Medications
	Time	BS	Cover	
	Time	BS	Cover	
	Time	BS	Cover	

Respiratory	Vitals		GI:	LABS	
Loungs/02	P	O2	Diet:	NA	WBC
	T	BP	Last BM:	PH	PLT
	R		GU:	K	TROPONIN
				PT/INR	CR
Edema :	**Skin :**		**Mobility :**	BUN	CA
				HGB	MG
Musculoskeletal :				OTHER	

Pain Assess :	Pain Reassess :	Blood Sugar :

Fluids:	Output:	Intake:	Notes :
DVT Pophylaxis:			

Plan of Care

Room	Admit Date	Situation	Attending Consult
Name	Allergies		
Age			
Sex	Code		

Hospital course	Present Illness	Precautions
	MD	

PMH : CA / CVA / DM / CHF / HTN / CKD / PVD / ESRD / Hypothyroid / Drug Abuse / PCI / Asthma / GERD / CAD / COPD / HLD / Psych / CKD / Smoker / Dementia / Other :

Tests/Procedures

Neuro	Neuro CIWA	Medical history					Lines
RASS		Meds/VF	Site	Size	Dose	Assessments	IV
NIH		1					CENTRAL
CAM		2					HD
A&O		3					Date
GCS		4					

Cardio/Tele	ACCU-CHECK			Medications
	Time	BS	Cover	
	Time	BS	Cover	
	Time	BS	Cover	

Respiratory	Vitals	GI:	LABS	
Lounge/02	P	Diet:	NA	WBC
	T O2	Last BM:	PH	PLT
	R BP	GU:	K	TROPONIN
			PT/INR	CR
Edema :	Skin :	Mobility :	BUN	CA
Musculoskeletal :			HGB	MG
			OTHER	

Pain Assess :	Pain Reassess :	Blood Sugar :

Fluids:	Output:	Intake:	Notes :

DVT Pophylaxis:

Plan of Care

Room	Admit Date	Situation	Attending Consult
Name	Allergies		
Age			
Sex	Code		

Hospital course	Present Illness	Precautions
	MD	

PMH : CA / CVA / DM / CHF / HTN / CKD / PVD / ESRD / Hypothyroid / Drug Abuse / PCI / Asthma / GERD / CAD / COPD / HLD / Psych / CKD / Smoker / Dementia / Other :

Tests/Procedures

Neuro	Neuro CIWA	Medical history					Lines
RASS		Meds/VF	Site	Size	Dose	Assessments	IV
NIH		1					CENTRAL
CAM		2					HD
A&O		3					Date
GCS		4					

Cardio/Tele	ACCU-CHECK			Medications
	Time	BS	Cover	
	Time	BS	Cover	
	Time	BS	Cover	

Respiratory		Vitals		GI:	LABS	
Loungs/02		P		Diet:	NA	WBC
			O2	Last BM:	PH	PLT
		T		GU:	K	TROPONIN
			BP		PT/INR	CR
		R			BUN	CA
Edema :		**Skin :**		**Mobility :**	HGB	MG
Musculoskeletal :					OTHER	

Pain Assess :	Pain Reassess :	Blood Sugar :

Fluids:	Output:	Intake:	Notes :
DVT Pophylaxis:			

Plan of Care

Room	Admit Date	Situation	Attending Consult
Name	Allergies		
Age			
Sex	Code		

Hospital course	Present Illness	Precautions
	MD	

PMH : CA / CVA / DM / CHF / HTN / CKD / PVD / ESRD / Hypothyroid / Drug Abuse / PCI / Asthma / GERD / CAD / COPD / HLD / Psych / CKD / Smoker / Dementia / Other :

Tests/Procedures

Neuro	Neuro CIWA	Medical history					Lines
RASS		Meds/VF	Site	Size	Dose	Assessments	IV
NIH		1					CENTRAL
CAM		2					HD
A&O		3					Date
GCS		4					

Cardio/Tele	ACCU-CHECK			Medications
	Time	BS	Cover	
	Time	BS	Cover	
	Time	BS	Cover	

Respiratory	Vitals		GI:	LABS	
Loungs/02	P		Diet:	NA	WBC
		O2	Last BM:	PH	PLT
	T		GU:	K	TROPONIN
		BP		PT/INR	CR
	R			BUN	CA

Edema :	Skin :	Mobility :	HGB	MG

Musculoskeletal :		OTHER

Pain Assess :	Pain Reassess :	Blood Sugar :

Fluids:	Output:	Intake:	Notes :

DVT Pophylaxis:	

Plan of Care

Room	Admit Date	Situation	Attending Consult
Name	**Allergies**		
Age			
Sex	**Code**		

Hospital course	Present Illness	Precautions
	MD	

PMH : CA / CVA / DM / CHF / HTN / CKD / PVD / ESRD / Hypothyroid / Drug Abuse / PCI / Asthma / GERD / CAD / COPD / HLD / Psych / CKD / Smoker / Dementia / Other :

Tests/Procedures

Neuro	Neuro CIWA	Medical history					Lines
RASS		Meds/VF	Site	Size	Dose	Assessments	IV
NIH		1					CENTRAL
CAM		2					HD
A&O		3					Date
GCS		4					

Cardio/Tele	ACCU-CHECK	Medications
	Time BS Cover	
	Time BS Cover	
	Time BS Cover	

Respiratory	Vitals	GI:	LABS	
Loungs/02	P O2	Diet:	NA	WBC
	T BP	Last BM:	PH	PLT
	R	GU:	K	TROPONIN
			PT/INR	CR
Edema :	**Skin :**	**Mobility :**	BUN	CA
Musculoskeletal :			HGB	MG
			OTHER	

Pain Assess :	Pain Reassess :	Blood Sugar :

Fluids:	Output:	Intake:	Notes :

DVT Pophylaxis:

Plan of Care

Room	Admit Date	Situation	Attending Consult
Name	Allergies		
Age			
Sex	Code		

Hospital course	Present Illness	Precautions
	MD	

PMH : CA / CVA / DM / CHF / HTN / CKD / PVD / ESRD / Hypothyroid / Drug Abuse / PCI / Asthma / GERD / CAD / COPD / HLD / Psych / CKD / Smoker / Dementia / Other :

Tests/Procedures

Neuro	Neuro CIWA	Medical history					Lines
RASS		Meds/VF	Site	Size	Dose	Assessments	IV
NIH		1					CENTRAL
CAM		2					HD
A&O		3					Date
GCS		4					

Cardio/Tele	ACCU-CHECK			Medications
	Time	BS	Cover	
	Time	BS	Cover	
	Time	BS	Cover	

Respiratory	Vitals	GI:	LABS	
Loungs/02	P	Diet:	NA	WBC
	T O2	Last BM:	PH	PLT
	BP	GU:	K	TROPONIN
	R		PT/INR	CR
Edema :	Skin :	Mobility :	BUN	CA
Musculoskeletal :			HGB	MG
			OTHER	

Pain Assess :	Pain Reassess :	Blood Sugar :

Fluids:	Output:	Intake:	Notes :
DVT Pophylaxis:			

Plan of Care

Room	Admit Date	Situation	Attending Consult
Name	**Allergies**		
Age			
Sex	**Code**		

Hospital course	Present Illness	Precautions
	MD	

PMH : CA / CVA / DM / CHF / HTN / CKD / PVD / ESRD / Hypothyroid / Drug Abuse / PCI / Asthma / GERD / CAD / COPD / HLD / Psych / CKD / Smoker / Dementia / Other :

Tests/Procedures

Neuro	Neuro CIWA	Medical history					Lines
RASS		Meds/VF	Site	Size	Dose	Assessments	IV
NIH		1					CENTRAL
CAM		2					HD
A&O		3					Date
GCS		4					

Cardio/Tele	ACCU-CHECK	Medications
	Time BS Cover	
	Time BS Cover	
	Time BS Cover	

Respiratory	Vitals	GI:	LABS	
Loungs/02	P O2	Diet:	NA	WBC
	T BP	Last BM:	PH	PLT
	R	GU:	K	TROPONIN
			PT/INR	CR
Edema :	**Skin :**	**Mobility :**	BUN	CA
Musculoskeletal :			HGB	MG
			OTHER	

Pain Assess :	Pain Reassess :	Blood Sugar :

Fluids:	Output:	Intake:	Notes :

DVT Pophylaxis:

Plan of Care

Room	Admit Date	Situation	Attending Consult
Name	**Allergies**		
Age			
Sex	**Code**		

Hospital course	Present Illness	Precautions
	MD	

PMH : CA / CVA / DM / CHF / HTN / CKD / PVD / ESRD / Hypothyroid / Drug Abuse / PCI / Asthma / GERD / CAD / COPD / HLD / Psych / CKD / Smoker / Dementia / Other :

Tests/Procedures

Neuro	Neuro CIWA	Medical history					Lines
RASS		Meds/VF	Site	Size	Dose	Assessments	IV
NIH		1					CENTRAL
CAM		2					HD
A&O		3					Date
GCS		4					

Cardio/Tele	ACCU-CHECK			Medications
	Time	BS	Cover	
	Time	BS	Cover	
	Time	BS	Cover	

Respiratory	Vitals		GI:	LABS	
Loungs/02	P	O2	Diet:	NA	WBC
	T	BP	Last BM:	PH	PLT
	R		GU:	K	TROPONIN
				PT/INR	CR
Edema :	Skin :		Mobility :	BUN	CA
Musculoskeletal :				HGB	MG
				OTHER	

Pain Assess :	Pain Reassess :	Blood Sugar :

Fluids:	Output:	Intake:	Notes :
DVT Pophylaxis:			

Plan of Care

Room	Admit Date	Situation	Attending Consult
Name	Allergies		
Age			
Sex	Code		

Hospital course	Present Illness	Precautions
	MD	

PMH : CA / CVA / DM / CHF / HTN / CKD / PVD / ESRD / Hypothyroid / Drug Abuse / PCI / Asthma / GERD / CAD / COPD / HLD / Psych / CKD / Smoker / Dementia / Other :

Tests/Procedures

Neuro	Neuro CIWA	Medical history					Lines
RASS		Meds/VF	Site	Size	Dose	Assessments	IV
NIH		1					CENTRAL
CAM		2					HD
A&O		3					Date
GCS		4					

Cardio/Tele	ACCU-CHECK	Medications
	Time BS Cover	
	Time BS Cover	
	Time BS Cover	

Respiratory	Vitals	GI:	LABS	
Loungs/02	P O2	Diet:	NA	WBC
	T BP	Last BM:	PH	PLT
	R	GU:	K	TROPONIN
			PT/INR	CR
Edema :	Skin :	Mobility :	BUN	CA
Musculoskeletal :			HGB	MG
			OTHER	

Pain Assess :	Pain Reassess :	Blood Sugar :

Fluids:	Output:	Intake:	Notes :
DVT Pophylaxis:			

Plan of Care

Room	Admit Date	Situation	Attending Consult
Name	**Allergies**		
Age			
Sex	**Code**		

Hospital course	Present Illness	Precautions
	MD	

PMH : CA / CVA / DM / CHF / HTN / CKD / PVD / ESRD / Hypothyroid / Drug Abuse / PCI / Asthma / GERD / CAD / COPD / HLD / Psych / CKD / Smoker / Dementia / Other :

Tests/Procedures

Neuro	Neuro CIWA	Medical history					Lines
RASS		Meds/VF	Site	Size	Dose	Assessments	IV
NIH		1					CENTRAL
CAM		2					HD
A&O		3					Date
GCS		4					

Cardio/Tele	ACCU-CHECK			Medications
	Time	BS	Cover	
	Time	BS	Cover	
	Time	BS	Cover	

Respiratory	Vitals	GI:	LABS	
Loungs/02	P	Diet:	NA	WBC
	O2	Last BM:	PH	PLT
	T	GU:	K	TROPONIN
	BP		PT/INR	CR
	R		BUN	CA

Edema :	Skin :	Mobility :	HGB	MG
Musculoskeletal :			OTHER	

Pain Assess :	Pain Reassess :	Blood Sugar :

Fluids:	Output:	Intake:	Notes :

DVT Pophylaxis:

Plan of Care

Room	Admit Date	Situation	Attending Consult
Name	Allergies		
Age			
Sex	Code		

Hospital course	Present Illness	Precautions
	MD	

PMH : CA / CVA / DM / CHF / HTN / CKD / PVD / ESRD / Hypothyroid / Drug Abuse / PCI / Asthma / GERD / CAD / COPD / HLD / Psych / CKD / Smoker / Dementia / Other :

Tests/Procedures

Neuro	Neuro CIWA	Medical history					Lines
RASS		Meds/VF	Site	Size	Dose	Assessments	IV
NIH		1					CENTRAL
CAM		2					HD
A&O		3					Date
GCS		4					

Cardio/Tele	ACCU-CHECK	Medications
	Time BS Cover	
	Time BS Cover	
	Time BS Cover	

Respiratory	Vitals	GI:	LABS	
Loungs/02	P O2	Diet:	NA	WBC
	T	Last BM:	PH	PLT
	R BP	GU:	K	TROPONIN
			PT/INR	CR
Edema :	Skin :	Mobility :	BUN	CA
Musculoskeletal :			HGB	MG
			OTHER	

Pain Assess :	Pain Reassess :	Blood Sugar :

Fluids:	Output:	Intake:	Notes :
DVT Pophylaxis:			

Plan of Care

Room	Admit Date	Situation	Attending Consult
Name	Allergies		
Age			
Sex	Code		

Hospital course	Present Illness	Precautions
	MD	

PMH : CA / CVA / DM / CHF / HTN / CKD / PVD / ESRD / Hypothyroid / Drug Abuse / PCI / Asthma / GERD / CAD / COPD / HLD / Psych / CKD / Smoker / Dementia / Other :

Tests/Procedures

Neuro	Neuro CIWA	Medical history					Lines
RASS		Meds/VF	Site	Size	Dose	Assessments	IV
NIH		1					CENTRAL
CAM		2					HD
A&O		3					Date
GCS		4					

Cardio/Tele	ACCU-CHECK			Medications
	Time	BS	Cover	
	Time	BS	Cover	
	Time	BS	Cover	

Respiratory	Vitals		GI:		LABS	
Lounges/02	P	O2	Diet:	NA		WBC
	T	BP	Last BM:	PH		PLT
	R		GU:	K		TROPONIN
				PT/INR		CR
Edema :	Skin :		Mobility :	BUN		CA
Musculoskeletal :				HGB		MG
				OTHER		

Pain Assess :	Pain Reassess :	Blood Sugar :

Fluids:	Output:	Intake:	Notes :
DVT Pophylaxis:			

Plan of Care

Room	Admit Date	Situation	Attending Consult
Name Age	**Allergies**		
Sex	**Code**		

Hospital course	Present Illness	Precautions
	MD	

PMH : CA / CVA / DM / CHF / HTN / CKD / PVD / ESRD / Hypothyroid / Drug Abuse / PCI / Asthma / GERD / CAD / COPD / HLD / Psych / CKD / Smoker / Dementia / Other :

Tests/Procedures

Neuro	Neuro CIWA	Medical history					Lines
RASS		Meds/VF	Site	Size	Dose	Assessments	IV
NIH		1					CENTRAL
CAM		2					HD
A&O		3					Date
GCS		4					

Cardio/Tele	ACCU-CHECK	Medications
	Time　　BS　　Cover	
	Time　　BS　　Cover	
	Time　　BS　　Cover	

Respiratory	Vitals	GI:	LABS	
Loungs/02	P　　　O2　　T　　　BP　　R	Diet:　　Last BM:　　**GU:**	NA	WBC
			PH	PLT
			K	TROPONIN
			PT/INR	CR
Edema :　　**Skin :**　　**Mobility :**			BUN	CA
Musculoskeletal :			HGB	MG
			OTHER	

Pain Assess :	Pain Reassess :	Blood Sugar :

Fluids:	Output:	Intake:	Notes :

DVT Pophylaxis:

Plan of Care

Room	Admit Date	Situation	Attending Consult
Name	Allergies		
Age			
Sex	Code		

Hospital course	Present Illness	Precautions
	MD	

PMH : CA / CVA / DM / CHF / HTN / CKD / PVD / ESRD / Hypothyroid / Drug Abuse / PCI / Asthma / GERD / CAD / COPD / HLD / Psych / CKD / Smoker / Dementia / Other :

Tests/Procedures

Neuro	Neuro CIWA	Medical history					Lines
RASS		Meds/VF	Site	Size	Dose	Assessments	IV
NIH		1					CENTRAL
CAM		2					HD
A&O		3					Date
GCS		4					

Cardio/Tele	ACCU-CHECK	Medications
	Time BS Cover	
	Time BS Cover	
	Time BS Cover	

Respiratory	Vitals	GI:	LABS	
Loungs/02	P O2	Diet:	NA	WBC
	T BP	Last BM:	PH	PLT
	R	GU:	K	TROPONIN
			PT/INR	CR
Edema :	Skin :	Mobility :	BUN	CA
Musculoskeletal :			HGB	MG
			OTHER	

Pain Assess :	Pain Reassess :	Blood Sugar :

Fluids:	Output:	Intake:	Notes :
DVT Pophylaxis:			

Plan of Care

Room	Admit Date	Situation	Attending Consult
Name	Allergies		
Age			
Sex	Code		

Hospital course	Present Illness	Precautions
	MD	

PMH : CA / CVA / DM / CHF / HTN / CKD / PVD / ESRD / Hypothyroid / Drug Abuse / PCI / Asthma / GERD / CAD / COPD / HLD / Psych / CKD / Smoker / Dementia / Other :

Tests/Procedures

Neuro	Neuro CIWA	Medical history					Lines
RASS		Meds/VF	Site	Size	Dose	Assessments	IV
NIH		1					CENTRAL
CAM		2					HD
A&O		3					Date
GCS		4					

Cardio/Tele	ACCU-CHECK	Medications
	Time BS Cover	
	Time BS Cover	
	Time BS Cover	

Respiratory	Vitals	GI:	LABS	
Loungs/02	P O2	Diet:	NA	WBC
	T BP	Last BM:	PH	PLT
	R	GU:	K	TROPONIN
			PT/INR	CR
Edema :	Skin :	Mobility :	BUN	CA
			HGB	MG
Musculoskeletal :			OTHER	

Pain Assess :	Pain Reassess :	Blood Sugar :

Fluids:	Output:	Intake:	Notes :
DVT Pophylaxis:			

Plan of Care

Room	Admit Date	Situation	Attending Consult
Name	Allergies		
Age			
Sex	Code		

Hospital course	Present Illness	Precautions
	MD	

PMH : CA / CVA / DM / CHF / HTN / CKD / PVD / ESRD / Hypothyroid / Drug Abuse / PCI / Asthma / GERD / CAD / COPD / HLD / Psych / CKD / Smoker / Dementia / Other :

Tests/Procedures

Neuro	Neuro CIWA	Medical history					Lines
RASS		Meds/VF	Site	Size	Dose	Assessments	IV
NIH		1					CENTRAL
CAM		2					HD
A&O		3					Date
GCS		4					

Cardio/Tele	ACCU-CHECK			Medications
	Time	BS	Cover	
	Time	BS	Cover	
	Time	BS	Cover	

Respiratory	Vitals	GI:	LABS	
Loungs/02	P	Diet:	NA	WBC
	O2	Last BM:	PH	PLT
	T	GU:	K	TROPONIN
	BP		PT/INR	CR
	R		BUN	CA

Edema :	Skin :	Mobility :	HGB	MG
Musculoskeletal :			OTHER	

Pain Assess :	Pain Reassess :	Blood Sugar :

Fluids:	Output:	Intake:	Notes :

DVT Pophylaxis:

Plan of Care

Room	Admit Date	Situation	Attending Consult
Name	Allergies		
Age			
Sex	Code		

Hospital course	Present Illness	Precautions
	MD	

PMH : CA / CVA / DM / CHF / HTN / CKD / PVD / ESRD / Hypothyroid / Drug Abuse / PCI / Asthma / GERD / CAD / COPD / HLD / Psych / CKD / Smoker / Dementia / Other :

Tests/Procedures

Neuro	Neuro CIWA	Medical history					Lines
RASS		Meds/VF	Site	Size	Dose	Assessments	IV
NIH		1					CENTRAL
CAM		2					HD
A&O		3					Date
GCS		4					

Cardio/Tele	ACCU-CHECK			Medications
	Time	BS	Cover	
	Time	BS	Cover	
	Time	BS	Cover	

Respiratory	Vitals	GI:	LABS	
Lounges/02	P	Diet:	NA	WBC
		O2		
	T	Last BM:	PH	PLT
		BP	GU:	K	TROPONIN
	R		PT/INR	CR

Edema :	Skin :	Mobility :	BUN	CA

Musculoskeletal :	HGB	MG
	OTHER	

Pain Assess :	Pain Reassess :	Blood Sugar :	

Fluids:	Output:	Intake:	Notes :

DVT Pophylaxis:

Plan of Care

Room	Admit Date	Situation	Attending Consult
Name	Allergies		
Age			
Sex	Code		

Hospital course	Present Illness	Precautions
	MD	

PMH : CA / CVA / DM / CHF / HTN / CKD / PVD / ESRD / Hypothyroid / Drug Abuse / PCI / Asthma / GERD / CAD / COPD / HLD / Psych / CKD / Smoker / Dementia / Other :

Tests/Procedures

Neuro	Neuro CIWA	Medical history					Lines
RASS		Meds/VF	Site	Size	Dose	Assessments	IV
NIH		1					CENTRAL
CAM		2					HD
A&O		3					Date
GCS		4					

Cardio/Tele	ACCU-CHECK			Medications
	Time	BS	Cover	
	Time	BS	Cover	
	Time	BS	Cover	

Respiratory	Vitals	GI:	LABS	
Loungs/02	P O2	Diet:	NA	WBC
	T BP	Last BM:	PH	PLT
	R	GU:	K	TROPONIN
			PT/INR	CR
Edema :	Skin :	Mobility :	BUN	CA
Musculoskeletal :			HGB	MG
			OTHER	

Pain Assess :	Pain Reassess :	Blood Sugar :

Fluids:	Output:	Intake:	Notes :
DVT Pophylaxis:			

Plan of Care

Room	Admit Date	Situation	Attending Consult
Name	Allergies		
Age			
Sex	Code		

Hospital course	Present Illness	Precautions
	MD	

PMH : CA / CVA / DM / CHF / HTN / CKD / PVD / ESRD / Hypothyroid / Drug Abuse / PCI / Asthma / GERD / CAD / COPD / HLD / Psych / CKD / Smoker / Dementia / Other :

Tests/Procedures

Neuro	Neuro CIWA	Medical history					Lines
RASS		Meds/VF	Site	Size	Dose	Assessments	IV
NIH		1					CENTRAL
CAM		2					HD
A&O		3					Date
GCS		4					

Cardio/Tele	ACCU-CHECK			Medications
	Time	BS	Cover	
	Time	BS	Cover	
	Time	BS	Cover	

Respiratory	Vitals	GI:	LABS	
Loungs/02	P	Diet:	NA	WBC
	T O2	Last BM:	PH	PLT
	BP	GU:	K	TROPONIN
	R		PT/INR	CR
Edema :	Skin :	Mobility :	BUN	CA
Musculoskeletal :			HGB	MG
			OTHER	

Pain Assess :	Pain Reassess :	Blood Sugar :

Fluids:	Output:	Intake:	Notes :
DVT Pophylaxis:			

Plan of Care

Room	Admit Date	Situation	Attending Consult
Name	Allergies		
Age			
Sex	Code		

Hospital course	Present Illness	Precautions
	MD	

PMH : CA / CVA / DM / CHF / HTN / CKD / PVD / ESRD / Hypothyroid / Drug Abuse / PCI / Asthma / GERD / CAD / COPD / HLD / Psych / CKD / Smoker / Dementia / Other :

Tests/Procedures

Neuro	Neuro CIWA	Medical history					Lines
RASS		Meds/VF	Site	Size	Dose	Assessments	IV
NIH		1					CENTRAL
CAM		2					HD
A&O		3					Date
GCS		4					

Cardio/Tele	ACCU-CHECK	Medications
	Time BS Cover	
	Time BS Cover	
	Time BS Cover	

Respiratory	Vitals	GI:	LABS	
Loungs/02	P O2	Diet:	NA	WBC
	T BP	Last BM:	PH	PLT
	R	GU:	K	TROPONIN
			PT/INR	CR
Edema : Skin :		Mobility :	BUN	CA
Musculoskeletal :			HGB	MG
			OTHER	

Pain Assess :	Pain Reassess :	Blood Sugar :

Fluids:	Output:	Intake:	Notes :
DVT Pophylaxis:			

Plan of Care

Room	Admit Date	Situation	Attending Consult
Name	Allergies		
Age			
Sex	Code		

Hospital course	Present Illness	Precautions
	MD	

PMH : CA / CVA / DM / CHF / HTN / CKD / PVD / ESRD / Hypothyroid / Drug Abuse / PCI / Asthma / GERD / CAD / COPD / HLD / Psych / CKD / Smoker / Dementia / Other :

Tests/Procedures

Neuro	Neuro CIWA	Medical history					Lines
RASS		Meds/VF	Site	Size	Dose	Assessments	IV
NIH		1					CENTRAL
CAM		2					HD
A&O		3					Date
GCS		4					

Cardio/Tele	ACCU-CHECK	Medications
	Time BS Cover	
	Time BS Cover	
	Time BS Cover	

Respiratory	Vitals	GI:	LABS	
Loungs/02	P O2	Diet:	NA	WBC
	T BP	Last BM:	PH	PLT
	R	GU:	K	TROPONIN
			PT/INR	CR
Edema :	Skin :	Mobility :	BUN	CA
Musculoskeletal :			HGB	MG
			OTHER	

Pain Assess :	Pain Reassess :	Blood Sugar :

Fluids:	Output:	Intake:	Notes :
DVT Pophylaxis:			

Plan of Care

Room	Admit Date	Situation	Attending Consult
Name	**Allergies**		
Age			
Sex	**Code**		

Hospital course	Present Illness	Precautions
	MD	

PMH : CA / CVA / DM / CHF / HTN / CKD / PVD / ESRD / Hypothyroid / Drug Abuse / PCI / Asthma / GERD / CAD / COPD / HLD / Psych / CKD / Smoker / Dementia / Other :

Tests/Procedures

Neuro	Neuro CIWA	Medical history					Lines
RASS		Meds/VF	Site	Size	Dose	Assessments	IV
NIH		1					CENTRAL
CAM		2					HD
A&O		3					Date
GCS		4					

Cardio/Tele	ACCU-CHECK			Medications
	Time	BS	Cover	
	Time	BS	Cover	
	Time	BS	Cover	

Respiratory	Vitals		GI:	LABS	
Loungs/02	P		Diet:	NA	WBC
		O2	Last BM:	PH	PLT
	T		GU:	K	TROPONIN
		BP		PT/INR	CR
	R			BUN	CA
Edema :	Skin :		Mobility :	HGB	MG
Musculoskeletal :				OTHER	

Pain Assess :	Pain Reassess :	Blood Sugar :

Fluids:	Output:	Intake:	Notes :
DVT Pophylaxis:			

Plan of Care

Room	Admit Date	Situation	Attending Consult
Name	Allergies		
Age			
Sex	Code		

Hospital course	Present Illness	Precautions
	MD	

PMH : CA / CVA / DM / CHF / HTN / CKD / PVD / ESRD / Hypothyroid / Drug Abuse / PCI / Asthma / GERD / CAD / COPD / HLD / Psych / CKD / Smoker / Dementia / Other :

Tests/Procedures

Neuro	Neuro CIWA	Medical history					Lines
RASS		Meds/VF	Site	Size	Dose	Assessments	IV
NIH		1					CENTRAL
CAM		2					HD
A&O		3					Date
GCS		4					

Cardio/Tele	ACCU-CHECK			Medications
	Time	BS	Cover	
	Time	BS	Cover	
	Time	BS	Cover	

Respiratory	Vitals	GI:	LABS	
Loungs/02	P O2	Diet:	NA	WBC
	T BP	Last BM:	PH	PLT
	R	GU:	K	TROPONIN
			PT/INR	CR
Edema :	Skin :	Mobility :	BUN	CA
Musculoskeletal :			HGB	MG
			OTHER	

Pain Assess :	Pain Reassess :	Blood Sugar :

Fluids:	Output:	Intake:	Notes :
DVT Pophylaxis:			

Plan of Care